# Edexcel GCSE (9-1)
# Mathematics
## Access to Foundation

Number Workbook

ALWAYS LEARNING

**PEARSON**

Published by Pearson Education Limited, 80 Strand, London WC2R 0RL.

www.pearsonschoolsandfecolleges.co.uk

Text © Pearson Education Limited 2015
Typeset and illustrated by Tek-Art, West Sussex
Original illustrations © Pearson Education Limited 2015
Cover created by Fusako
Photography by NanaAkua

The right of Bobbie Johns, Su Nicholson and Glyn Payne to be identified as authors of this work has been asserted by them in accordance with the Copyright, Designs and Patents Act 1988.

First published 2015

17 16 15
10 9 8 7 6 5 4 3 2

**British Library Cataloguing in Publication Data**
A catalogue record for this book is available from the British Library

ISBN 978 1 447 98358 3

Printed in Slovakia by Neografia

**Acknowledgements**
Every effort has been made to contact copyright holders of material reproduced in this book. Any omissions will be rectified in subsequent printings if notice is given to the publishers.

**A note from the publisher**
In order to ensure that this resource offers high-quality support for the associated Edexcel qualification, it has been through a review process by the awarding body to confirm that it fully covers the teaching and learning content of the specification or part of a specification at which it is aimed, and demonstrates an appropriate balance between the development of subject skills, knowledge and understanding, in addition to preparation for assessment.

While the publishers have made every attempt to ensure that advice on the qualification and its assessment is accurate, the official specification and associated assessment guidance materials are the only authoritative source of information and should always be referred to for definitive guidance. Edexcel examiners have not contributed to any sections in this resource relevant to examination papers for which they have responsibility. No material from an endorsed resource will be used verbatim in any assessment set by Edexcel.

Endorsement of a resource does not mean that the resource is required to achieve this Edexcel qualification, nor does it mean that it is the only suitable material available to support the qualification, and any resource lists produced by the awarding body shall include this and other appropriate resources.

---

## Notices

The calculator symbol shows questions where:
- calculator skills are being developed, or
- using a calculator effectively is an important aspect of answering the question, or
- the calculation exceeds the scope of written methods in earlier chapters.

# Contents

# Self-assessment chart

| | Need more practice | Almost there | Got it! | |
|---|---|---|---|---|
| **Unit 1 Integers (1)** | | | | Step |
| 1.1 Read, write, order and compare positive integers | ☐ | ☐ | ☐ | ➡ 1st |
| 1.2 Add and subtract positive integers | ☐ | ☐ | ☐ | ➡ 2nd |
| 1.3 Multiply and divide by 10, 100 and 1000 | ☐ | ☐ | ☐ | ➡ 2nd |
| 1.4 Multiplication and division facts up to $10 \times 10$ | ☐ | ☐ | ☐ | ➡ 2nd |
| 1.5 Multiply and divide by a single digit | ☐ | ☐ | ☐ | ➡ 2nd |
| 1.6 Round to the nearest 10, 100 and 1000 | ☐ | ☐ | ☐ | ➡ 2nd |
| 1.7 Find multiples and factors and identify prime numbers | ☐ | ☐ | ☐ | ➡ 3rd |
| 1.8 Understand and use negative numbers | ☐ | ☐ | ☐ | ➡ 3rd |
| **Unit 2 Order of operations** | | | | |
| 2.1 Order of operations | ☐ | ☐ | ☐ | ➡ 2nd |
| **Unit 3 Decimals (1)** | | | | |
| 3.1 Read, write and order decimals | ☐ | ☐ | ☐ | ➡ 3rd |
| 3.2 Add and subtract simple decimals | ☐ | ☐ | ☐ | ➡ 3rd |
| 3.3 Multiply and divide decimal numbers | ☐ | ☐ | ☐ | ➡ 4th |
| 3.4 Rounding decimals | ☐ | ☐ | ☐ | ➡ 3rd |
| **Unit 4 Approximations (1)** | | | | |
| 4.1 Check solutions | ☐ | ☐ | ☐ | ➡ 4th |
| **Unit 5 Fractions (1)** | | | | |
| 5.1 Read, write and order fractions | ☐ | ☐ | ☐ | ➡ 2nd |
| 5.2 Use equivalent fractions | ☐ | ☐ | ☐ | ➡ 2nd |
| 5.3 Write fractions in their simplest form | ☐ | ☐ | ☐ | ➡ 3rd |
| 5.4 Convert between fractions and decimals | ☐ | ☐ | ☐ | ➡ 3rd |
| 5.5 Add and subtract fractions | ☐ | ☐ | ☐ | ➡ 2nd |
| 5.6 Find fractions of quantities | ☐ | ☐ | ☐ | ➡ 3rd |
| **Unit 6 Percentages (1)** | | | | |
| 6.1 Decimals, fractions and percentages | ☐ | ☐ | ☐ | ➡ 4th |
| 6.2 Order and compare percentages | ☐ | ☐ | ☐ | ➡ 4th |
| 6.3 Find percentages of quantities | ☐ | ☐ | ☐ | ➡ 4th |
| **Unit 7 Money** | | | | |
| 7.1 Read and order amounts of money | ☐ | ☐ | ☐ | ➡ 2nd |
| 7.2 Calculating with money | ☐ | ☐ | ☐ | ➡ 3rd |
| **Unit 8 Time** | | | | |
| 8.1 Read, record and measure time | ☐ | ☐ | ☐ | ➡ 1st |
| 8.2 Use units of time | ☐ | ☐ | ☐ | ➡ 3rd |
| 8.3 Convert between units of time | ☐ | ☐ | ☐ | ➡ 3rd |
| 8.4 Use calendars | ☐ | ☐ | ☐ | ➡ 3rd |
| **Unit 9 Integers (2)** | | | | |
| 9.1 Read, write, order and compare integers | ☐ | ☐ | ☐ | ➡ 2nd |
| 9.2 Add and subtract integers | ☐ | ☐ | ☐ | ➡ 3rd |
| 9.3 Multiply and divide integers | ☐ | ☐ | ☐ | ➡ 3rd |
| 9.4 Multiply and divide using negative integers | ☐ | ☐ | ☐ | ➡ 4th |
| 9.5 Read, write and use squares, cubes and square roots | ☐ | ☐ | ☐ | ➡ 4th |
| 9.6 Use index notation | ☐ | ☐ | ☐ | ➡ 4th |
| **Unit 10 Function machines** | | | | |
| 10.1 Function machines | ☐ | ☐ | ☐ | ➡ 3rd |
| **Unit 11 Decimals (2)** | | | | |
| 11.1 Multiply and divide decimals | ☐ | ☐ | ☐ | ➡ 4th |
| 11.2 Round decimals | ☐ | ☐ | ☐ | ➡ 3rd |
| 11.3 Add and subtract any decimals | ☐ | ☐ | ☐ | ➡ 4th |

| | Need more practice | Almost there | Got it! | | Step |
|---|---|---|---|---|---|
| **Unit 12 Approximations (2)** | | | | | |
| 12.1 Round to one significant figure | ☐ | ☐ | ☐ | ➜ | 4th |
| 12.2 Estimate answers | ☐ | ☐ | ☐ | ➜ | 4th |
| **Unit 13 Fractions (2)** | | | | | |
| 13.1 Use fractions to compare quantities | ☐ | ☐ | ☐ | ➜ | 4th |
| 13.2 Express one number as a fraction of another | ☐ | ☐ | ☐ | ➜ | 4th |
| **Unit 14 Percentages (2)** | | | | | |
| 14.1 Find percentages of quantities | ☐ | ☐ | ☐ | ➜ | 4th |
| 14.2 Write one number as a percentage of another | ☐ | ☐ | ☐ | ➜ | 4th |
| **Unit 15 Direct proportion** | | | | | |
| 15.1 Use direct proportion | ☐ | ☐ | ☐ | ➜ | 4th |
| **Unit 16 Algebra** | | | | | |
| 16.1 Simplifying algebraic expressions | ☐ | ☐ | ☐ | ➜ | 3rd |
| 16.2 Using a formula given in words | ☐ | ☐ | ☐ | ➜ | 2nd |
| 16.3 Using an algebraic formula | ☐ | ☐ | ☐ | ➜ | 4th |

# Introduction

Helping you prepare for *Edexcel GCSE (9-1) Mathematics – Foundation*, this workbook is a good way to refresh your learning on Number (and a little Algebra).

Work your way through this book unit by unit:

* ✳ The clear **learning objectives** help you focus
* ✳ The **key points** give you reminders
* ✳ The **worked examples** guide you through to the solution
* ✳ All the carefully stepped **practice** develops your confidence
* ✳ Stretch yourself a bit with **extend** questions
* ✳ The unit **summaries** help you recap and revise
* ✳ Take the **unit tests** to check your fluency and build your confidence
* ✳ Take the **Number Test** at the end of the book to check your progress.

And there's a useful self-assessment chart on pages iv-v for you to fill in as you go!

## Geometry and Statistics

As further preparation alongside Number, before you progress on to the Foundation GCSE course, you could also refresh your learning in geometry and measures, statistics and probability.

# Read, write, order and compare positive integers

**1.1**

By the end of this section you will know how to:

* ✳ Read, write, order and compare positive integers up to 1000

**Key points**

> **Hint**
> An **integer** is a positive or negative whole number including zero.

* ✳ The value of each digit depends on its place in the number.
* ✳ A 3-digit whole number is always larger than a 2-digit whole number.

**Example**

**1 a** Read and write **456** in words.

| Hundreds | Tens | Units |
|----------|------|-------|
| 4 | 5 | 6 |
| 400 | 50 | 6 |

= four .................... and ............. – ............

**b** Read and write **509** in words.

| Hundreds | Tens | Units |
|----------|------|-------|
| 5 | 0 | 9 |
| ........... | 0 | ........... |

= ...............................................

**2** Write these numbers in words. Use the words in question 1 to help you.

**a** 274 ..................................... hundred and ...........................................

**b** 350 three ............................ and ...........................................

**c** 605 ......................................................................................

**d** 418 ......................................................................................

**e** 999 ......................................................................................

> **Hint**
> Writing a number in figures is the same as writing it in numerals or digits.

**Practice**

**3** Write these numbers in figures.

**a** four hundred and ninety-seven ..............    **b** three hundred and nineteen ..............

**c** eight hundred and three ..............    **d** nine hundred and thirty ..............

**Example**

**4** Partition (split up) these numbers into hundreds, tens and units.

**a** 386 = 300 + ....0.... + ...........  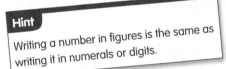    **b** 405 = 4........ + .......... + ..........

**c** 710 = .......... + .......... + ..........    **d** 942 = .......... + ....... + ..........

**Practice**

**5** Partition these numbers.

**a** 829 ..........................................    **b** 471 ..........................................

**c** 620 ..........................................    **d** 706 ..........................................

## Comparing and ordering numbers

**Example**

**6** Use the words 'is greater than' or 'is less than' to compare these numbers.

**a** 27 is less than 45

**b** 81 is ............... than 78

**c** 48 is .............................. 51

**d** 376 .............................. 457

**e** 730 .............................. 489

**f** 701 .............................. 699

**Practice**

**7** Write these numbers in order.

**a** 465    639    285    313    smallest .............................................. largest

**b** 673    763    637    736    smallest .............................................. largest

**c** 451    423    432    415    largest .............................................. smallest

**8 a** What is the largest number you can make with the digits ④, ⑨ and ③?

**b** What is the smallest number you can make with the digits ④, ⑨ and ③?

**c** What is the nearest number to 400 you can make with the digits ④, ⑨ and ③?

**Extend**

**9 a** In the number **3756** what is the value of the 7? ..... Seven hunded

**b** Write the number **4708** in words. ..............................................

**c** Write the number **nine thousand, four hundred and seventeen** in numerals. ..............

Need more practice ☐    Almost there ☐    Got it! ☐

# 1.2 Add and subtract positive integers

By the end of this section you will know how to:
* Add and subtract positive integers

## Key points

* Digits of the same place value must be added together.
* When adding or subtracting in columns, digits of the same place value must be lined up carefully.

**1** Look for number bonds to 10 and other multiples of 10 to add these numbers.

**Hint**

Addition can be done in any order, but this is not true for subtraction.

**a** 23 + 37 = 20 + 30 + 3 + 7 = 50 + .......... = ..........

**b** 46 + 54 = 40 + .......... + .......... + .......... = .......... + .......... = ..........

**c** 25 + 32 + 45 = 25 + 45 + 32 = .......... + .......... + .......... + .......... + .......... = .......... + .......... = ..........

**2** Work out these subtraction calculations using a number line to help you.

**a** 24 − 17 = ..................

+3 +4 = 7

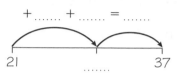

10      17  20  24      30

**b** 37 − 21 = ..................

+ .......... + .......... = ..........

21 .......... 37

**c** 45 − 25 = ..................

25                    45

**d** 78 − 24 = ..................

**e** 43 − 29 = ..................

**f** 84 − 16 = ..................

**3** Write the pairs of numbers that add together to make 100.

| 81 | 31 | 19 | 93 |
|----|----|----|----|
| 79 | 7  | 59 | 9  |
| 21 | 41 | 91 | 69 |

.............. + .............. = 100          .............. + .............. = 100

.............. + .............. = 100          .............. + .............. = 100

.............. + .............. = 100          .............. + .............. = 100

**4** Find the totals of these pairs of numbers by writing the digits in columns to add them.

**a** 254 + 462

```
  H  T  U
  7  2  6
+ 3  8  6
---------
        2
     1
```

**Hint**

Write the ten as a 1 underneath the tens column.

**b** 726 + 386

```
  H  T  U
  2  5  4
+ 4  6  2
---------
   .. 1  6
     1
```

**c** 477 + 65

```
  H  T  U
  4  7  7
+    6  5
---------
        2
     1
```

**5** Add these pairs of numbers.

**a** 285 + 562

**b** 275 + 691

**c** 365 + 726

**d** 864 + 69

**e** 297 + 604

**f** 758 + 65

**Example**

**6** Work out these subtraction calculations.

**a** 735 − 291

```
    H   T   U
    ⁶7̶  ¹3  5
 −  2   9   1
 ─────────────
        4   4
```

**b** 802 − 578

```
    H   T   U
    8   0   ¹2
 −  5   7   8
 ─────────────
            4
```

**c** 317 − 64

```
    H   T   U
    3   ¹1  7
 −      6   4
 ─────────────
        5   3
```

**Practice**

**7** Find the difference between these pairs of numbers.

**Hint**

Find the **difference** by doing subtraction.

**a** 572 − 284

**b** 706 − 456

**c** 900 − 274

**d** 347 − 23

**e** 322 − 78

**f** 504 − 58

**Extend**

**8** Work out the answers.

**a** In Year 10 there are 567 students and in Year 11 there are 489 students. What is the total number of students in Years 10 and 11?

..............................

**b** Sally has 821 friends on MyPals and Steve has 765. How many more friends does Sally have?

..............................

**c** Add together 265, 542 and 64.

..............................

# 1.3 Multiply and divide by 10, 100 and 1000

By the end of this section you will know how to:

* Multiply integers by 10, 100 and 1000
* Divide multiples of 10, 100 and 1000 by 10, 100 and 1000

## Key points

* Multiplying a number by 10, 100 or 1000 means that each digit moves in place value to the left.
* Dividing a number by 10, 100 or 1000 means that each digit moves in place value to the right.

**Example**

**1** Work out the answers to these multiplications.

a  $34 \times 10 = 340$

b  $123 \times 10 = $ ...............

c  $560 \times 100 = $ ...............

d  $37 \times 1000 = $ ...............

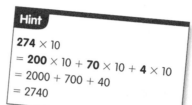

Hint

$274 \times 10$
$= 200 \times 10 + 70 \times 10 + 4 \times 10$
$= 2000 + 700 + 40$
$= 2740$

Hint

10 times table facts and related divisions.

**Practice**

**2** Work out the answers to these multiplications.

a  $57 \times 10 = $ ...............

b  $583 \times 10 = $ ...............

c  $120 \times 10 = $ ...............

d  $6 \times 100 = $ ...............

e  $72 \times 100 = $ ...............

f  $376 \times 100 = $ ...............

g  $60 \times 1000 = $ ...............

h  $752 \times 1000 = $ ...............

i  $360 \times 1000 = $ ...............

**Example**

**3** Work out the answers to these divisions.

a  $120 \div 10 = 12$

b  $2650 \div 10 = $ ...............

c  $4800 \div 100 = $ ...............

d  $7000 \div 1000 = $ ...............

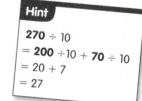

Hint

$270 \div 10$
$= 200 \div 10 + 70 \div 10$
$= 20 + 7$
$= 27$

**Practice**

**4** Work out the answers to these divisions.

a  $50 \div 10 = $ ...............

b  $290 \div 10 = $ ...............

c  $5000 \div 10 = $ ...............

d  $400 \div 100 = $ ...............

e  $6000 \div 100 = $ ...............

f  $2500 \div 100 = $ ...............

g  $8300 \div 100 = $ ...............

h  $3000 \div 1000 = $ ...............

i  $12\,000 \div 1000 = $ ...............

**5** Use the numbers in the cloud to give the answers to the following calculations.

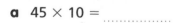

45    450    4500    45 000

a  $45 \times 10 = $ ...............

b  $450 \div 10 = $ ...............

c  $45 \times 100 = $ ...............

d  $4500 \div 10 = $ ...............

e  $4500 \div 100 = $ ...............

f  $45 \times 1000 = $ ...............

g  $45\,000 \div 1000 = $ ...............

h  $45\,000 \div 100 = $ ...............

**Extend**

**6** a  Write a matching multiplication and division.    $720 = $ ............ $\times$ ............ $= $ ............ $\div$ ............

b  Fill in the missing number.    $63 \times $ ............ $= 6300$

c  Fill in the missing number.    ............ $\div 1000 = 32$

# 1.4 Multiplication and division facts up to 10 × 10

By the end of this section you will know how to:

* Use the divisions related to multiplication facts

## Key points

* Multiplication and division are **inverse operations**.

**Practice**

**1** How many of these calculations can you do in 3 minutes?

**a** 3 × 4 = ............　　6 × 4 = ............　　2 × 9 = ............　　5 × 6 = ............

7 × 3 = ............　　5 × 9 = ............　　4 × 7 = ............　　5 × 5 = ............

6 × 6 = ............　　4 × 9 = ............　　5 × 8 = ............　　9 × 9 = ............

**b** 12 ÷ 4 = ........　　24 ÷ 6 = ........　　18 ÷ 2 = ........　　30 ÷ 6 = ........

21 ÷ 3 = ........　　45 ÷ 5 = ........　　28 ÷ ........ = 4　　25 ÷ ........ = 5

............ ÷ 6 = 6　　............ ÷ 4 = 9　　............ ÷ 8 = 5　　81 ÷ ........ = 9

**Example**

**2** Write the family of four related facts.

**a** 4 × 5 = 20　　5 × 4 = ............　　20 ÷ 4 = ........　　20 ÷ ........ = ............

**b** 7 × 4 = 28　　4 × ........ = ............　　28 ÷ ........ = ........　　28 ÷ ........ = ............

**c** 15 ÷ 3 = 5　　15 ÷ ........ = ........　　3 × ........ = ............　　........ × ........ = 15

**Practice**

**3** Work out the answer. Then complete the family of related facts.

**a** 24 ÷ 8 = ............　　............ ÷ ........ = ........　　........ × ........ = ............　　........ × ........ = ............

**b** 6 × 9 = ............　　........ × ........ = ............　　........ ÷ ........ = ............　　........ ÷ ........ = ............

**c** 63 ÷ 7 = ............　　........ ÷ ........ = ............　　........ × ........ = ............　　........ × ........ = ............

**Example**

**4** Split the multiple of 10 into a single digit × 10 to work out the answer to these multiplications.

**a** 2 × 30 = 2 × 3 × 10 = ........ × 10 = ............

**b** 4 × 30 = 4 × ........ × ........ = ........ × ........ = ............

**Practice**

**5** Work out the answers.

    **a** $6 \times 40 =$ .................................................................

    **b** $7 \times 30 =$ .................................................................

    **c** $50 \times 9 =$ .................................................................

    **d** $90 \times 8 =$ .................................................................

**Extend**

**6** $124 \times 5 = 620$   Use this fact to find the answers.

    **a** $5 \times 124 =$ ................

    **b** $620 \div 124 =$ ................

    **c** $124 \times 50 =$ ................

---

Need more practice  ☐    Almost there  ☐    Got it!  ☐

# Multiply and divide by a single digit

By the end of this section you will know how to:

* Multiply positive integers by a single digit
* Divide positive integers by a single digit

## Key points

* Numbers can be partitioned (split) into different place values to multiply them.

**Example**

**1** Work out the answers to these multiplications.

    **a** $241 \times 5$        **b** $253 \times 6$        **c** $379 \times 4$

| $\times$ | 5 |
|---|---|
| 200 | 1000 |
| 40 | 200 |
| 1 | 5 |

$+$

$241 \times 5 =$ ............

**Practice**

**2** Work out the answers.

    **a** $26 \times 4$        **b** $48 \times 3$        **c** $85 \times 7$

    **d** $218 \times 5$        **e** $523 \times 6$        **f** $403 \times 9$

**Example**

3 Complete these division calculations.

a 724 ÷ 4 = 181

$$\begin{array}{r} 1\;8\;1 \\ 4\overline{\smash{\big)}\,7\,{}^32\,4} \end{array}$$

b 675 ÷ 5 = ..................

$$5\overline{\smash{\big)}\,6\;7\;5}$$

c 510 ÷ 3 = ..................

$$3\overline{\smash{\big)}\,5\;1\;0}$$

**Practice**

4 Work out the answers to these division calculations.

a 632 ÷ 4 = ..................

b 735 ÷ 5 = ..................

c 804 ÷ 6 = ..................

d 486 ÷ 3 = ..................

e 612 ÷ 9 = ..................

f 413 ÷ 7 = ..................

**Extend**

5 There are 240 pupils in Year 10 to be divided equally between 8 classes. How many pupils will be in each class?

..................................

6 a Work out   2732 ÷ 4

b Work out   3366 ÷ 9

..................................

..................................

Need more practice ☐   Almost there ☐   Got it! ☐

# 1.6 Round to the nearest 10, 100 and 1000

By the end of this section you will know how to:

∗ Round positive integers to the nearest 10, 100 and 1000

**Key points**

∗ Round to the nearest 10:  round 5, 6, 7, 8 and 9 up; round 1, 2, 3 and 4 down.

∗ Round to the nearest 100: round 50, 60, 70, 80 and 90 up; round 10, 20, 30 and 40 down.

∗ Round to the nearest 1000: round 500, 600, 700, 800 and 900 up; round 100, 200, 300 and 400 down.

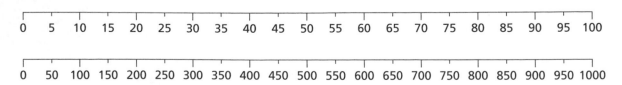

**Example**

1  The table shows the distances by road from London to different cities in miles and kilometres. Round the distances in miles to the nearest 10 miles and nearest 100 miles. Use the first number line on page 8 to help you round to the nearest 10 and the second number line to help round to the nearest 100. Record your answers in the table.

| Town | Distance (miles) | Nearest 10 miles | Nearest 100 miles | Distance (km) | Nearest 10 km | Nearest 100 km |
|------|------------------|------------------|-------------------|---------------|---------------|----------------|
| Bangor | 267 | 270 | 300 | 428 | | |
| Birmingham | 118 | 120 | 00 | 189 | | |
| Bristol | 121 | | | 193 | | |
| Cardiff | 153 | | | 225 | | |
| Glasgow | 405 | | | 647 | | |
| Manchester | 197 | | | 314 | | |

**Practice**

2  Now round the distances in question 1 to the nearest 10 km and nearest 100 km, using the number lines to help you. Record your answers in the table.

**Extend**

3  Look at the census form. Give an approximate population for these villages, by rounding each one to the nearest 1000. Use the number line below to help you.

| Town | Population |
|------|-----------|
| Lakeside | 2861 |
| Fieldcourt | 7239 |
| Castle Hill | 4356 |
| Millbrook | 4653 |
| Meadow Bank | 7803 |
| Broadoak | 739 |

Lakeside .............................
Fieldcourt .............................
Castle Hill .............................
Millbrook .............................
Meadow Bank .............................
Broadoak .............................

0  500 1000 1500 2000 2500 3000 3500 4000 4500 5000 5500 6000 6500 7000 7500 8000 8500 9000 9500 10000

Need more practice ☐    Almost there ☐    Got it! ☐

# 1.7  Find multiples and factors and identify prime numbers

By the end of this section you will know how to:
* Use the terms **multiple, factor, common factor** and **prime number**

**Key points**

* **Factors** of a number divide into that number exactly.
* Two factors of a number that multiply together to make that number are called a **factor pair**.
* A **multiple** of a number is in the times table of that number.
* A **prime number** has only two factors – itself and 1.

**Example**

1 Complete the multiplication grid. It has been started for you.

| × | 2 | 3 | 4 | 5 | 6 | 7 | 8 | 9 | 10 |
|---|---|---|---|---|---|---|---|---|---|
| 2 | 4 | 6 | 8 | | 12 | | 16 | 18 | |
| 3 | 6 | 9 | 12 | 15 | | 21 | | | 30 |
| 4 | 8 | 12 | 16 | | 24 | | | 36 | |
| 5 | | | 20 | | | 35 | | | |
| 6 | 12 | 18 | | | 36 | | | 54 | |
| 7 | | | | | 42 | | 56 | | 70 |
| 8 | | 24 | 32 | | | | | 72 | |
| 9 | | 27 | | 45 | | 63 | | | 90 |
| 10 | 20 | | | 50 | | | 80 | | |

**Practice**

2 a Write down the multiples of 5 from the grid. ........................................................

b Write down the multiples of 6 from the grid. ........................................................

c Write down the multiples of 9 from the grid. ........................................................

**Example**

3 Find the factor pairs of 12, 30 and 16 by writing the pairs of numbers that multiply together to make that number.

a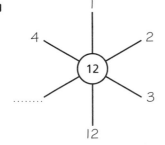

b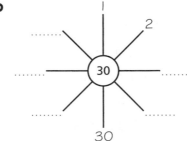

c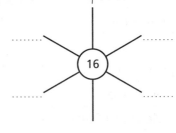

**Practice**

4 Use your answers in question 3 to write down the factors in order, from smallest to largest.

a Factors of 12: ................................................................

b Factors of 30: ................................................................

c Factors of 16: ................................................................

**Hint**

You only list each number once, even if you need to multiply a number by itself to get the number in the middle.

## Common factors and prime numbers

**Practice**

5 Look at the list of factors you made for 12, 30 and 16 in question 4. Write down the numbers that appear in both lists to show the common factors of these pairs of numbers.

a The common factors of 12 and 30 are ................................................................

b The common factors of 30 and 16 are ................................................................

c The common factors of 12 and 16 are ................................................................

**Hint**

The **common factors** of two numbers are numbers that appear in the list of factors of both numbers.

**Extend**

**6** Write the largest number in question 5 to show the highest common factor (HCF) of the pairs of numbers.

**Hint**

The **highest common factor** is often shortened to **HCF**.

a The HCF of 12 and 30 is .........................................................................................

b The HCF of 30 and 16 is .........................................................................................

c The HCF of 12 and 16 is .........................................................................................

**Practice**

**7** Look at the multiplication grid on the top of page 10 and at the numbers below. Put a ring around the numbers below that do *not* appear as answers in the multiplication grid – they are prime numbers because they only appear in their own multiplication table and only have one pair of factors.

**Hint**

**Prime numbers** have only two factors – the number itself and 1. 1 is not a prime number because it only has one factor.

| | 2 | 3 | 4 | 5 | 6 | 7 | 8 | 9 | 10 |
|---|---|---|---|---|---|---|---|---|---|
| 11 | 12 | 13 | 14 | 15 | 16 | 17 | 18 | 19 | 20 |
| 21 | 22 | 23 | 24 | 25 | 26 | 27 | 28 | 29 | 30 |

**Extend**

**8** Choose the correct number from the box.
Complete part **e** by writing a description for the numbers left over, using 'factor' or 'multiple'.

```
4        11
    10
15       18
    45
```

a A multiple of 6 ...............................................

b A factor of 16 ...............................    c A prime number ...............................

d A common factor of 20 and 30 ...............    e ............... is a ............................... of ...............

Need more practice ☐    Almost there ☐    Got it! ☐

# Understand and use negative numbers

**1.8**

By the end of this section you will know how to:

\* Read, order, add and subtract negative numbers

## Key points

\* Integers can be positive or negative or zero.

\* Numbers less than zero are called **negative numbers**.

\* In temperature a negative reading means the temperature is below zero and is very cold.

**Example**

**1** What temperature does each arrow show?

**Hint**

Negative whole numbers and zero are also integers.

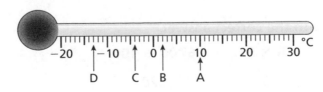

A 10°C        B .............°C        C −4°C        D .............°C

**Practice**

**2 a** Each temperature in question 1 rises by 4°. What is the new temperature?

A ............°C          B ............°C          C ............°C          D ............°C

**b** Each temperature in question 1 falls by 2°. What is the new temperature?

A ............°C          B ............°C          C ............°C          D ............°C

**3**

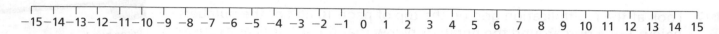

**a** Order these numbers from lowest to highest: 9, −4, 6, 0, −2. ..................................................

**b** Order these numbers from highest to lowest: −11, 7, 0, 3, −8. ..................................................

**Example**

**4** Use the number lines to help you add and subtract negative numbers.

          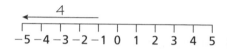

**a** 4 more than −5 = −1          **b** 4 less than −1 = ............          **c** 5 more than −5 = ............

**d** 6 less than 2 = ............          **e** 4 more than −1 = ............          **f** 3 less than −1 = ............

**Extend**

**5** Work out the answers.

**a** −4 + 2 = ............          **b** 3 − 6 = ............          **c** −2 − 4 = ............

**d** −2 + 2 = ............          **e** 0 − 10 = ............          **f** −3 − 8 = ............

---

**Don't forget!**

✳ Draw a line to match each term with its definition.

| integer | negative number | multiple of 10 | factor | prime number |
|---|---|---|---|---|
| number that divides exactly into another number | number less than zero | whole number | number divisible only by itself and 1 | number in the 10 times table |

✳ Match each calculation with the correct answer.

−3 + 5          2 − 5          −5 + 3          −1 − 4

−5          −2          2          −3

✳ Match each calculation with the correct answer.

54 ÷ 6          62 × 10          8 × 9          6200 ÷ 100

72          62          9          620

✳ When rounding to the nearest hundred, if a number ends in 50, 60, 70, 80 or 90, you round ............

and if the number ends in 10, 20, 30 or 40, you round ............

## Unit test

**1 a** Work out   24 × 10          **b** Work out   640 ÷ 10          **c** Work out   3600 ÷ 10

........................          ........................          ........................

**2 a** Work out

```
      6   5   7
  +   2   9   4
  _____
```

**b** Work out

```
      7   1   6
  -   3   7   2
  _____
```

**3 a** Work out   256 × 4          **b** Work out   342 ÷ 6

........................          ........................

**4 a** Write the number **367** in words. ................................................................

**b** Write **367** to the nearest ten. ........................   **c** Write **367** to the nearest hundred. ........................

**5** Write these numbers in order of size. Start with the smallest number.

**a** 285, 258, 528, 399 ........................          **b** 6, −3, 8, 0, −11 ........................

**6** Here is a list of numbers.   | 6   7   9   10   12   14   15   16   19 |

From the list

**a** write two multiples of 5 ............ ............          **b** write two prime numbers ........ ........

**c** write two factors of 24 ........ ........          **d** write two numbers that add to 30 ........ ........

**e** a common factor of 18 and 27 ........

**7 a**    Write down the reading of each mark on the thermometer.

A .......... °C          B .......... °C

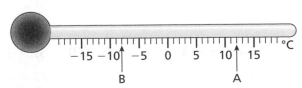

**b** On thermometer C show a reading of 5°C.

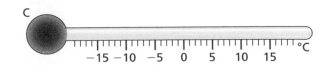

**c** On thermometer D show a reading of −2°C.

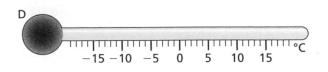

# Order of operations

## 2.1

By the end of this section you will know how to:

* Work out answers to calculations using mathematical operations in the correct order

### Key points

* BIDMAS helps you to remember the correct order of operations.

   **Brackets**    in any calculations, brackets must be worked out first

   **Indices**    indices means powers, e.g. $3^2 = 3 \times 3 = 9$, $2^4 = 2 \times 2 \times 2 \times 2 = 16$

   **Divide**    divide and multiply are of equal importance and can be done in any order

   **Multiply**

   **Add**    add and subtract are of equal importance and can be done in any order

   **Subtract**    but must be done after divide and multiply

* If there are several divide-and-multiply operations, do them one at a time, working from left to right.

* If there are several add-and-subtract operations, do them one at a time, working from left to right.

**Example**

**1** Work out

**a** $6 + 4 \times 5 - 2$

$= 6 + 20 - 2$

$= 24$

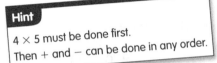

**Hint**

$4 \times 5$ must be done first.

Then + and − can be done in any order.

**b** $6 + 4 \times (5 - 2)$

$= 6 + 4 \times 3$

$= 6 + \ldots\ldots$

$= \ldots\ldots$

**Hint**

Bracket first.

**2** Work out

**a** $5 + 3^2 - 4$

$= 5 + 9 - 4$

$= \ldots\ldots$

**Hint**

Indices first, $3^2 = 3 \times 3 = 9$

**b** $(5 + 3)^2 - 4$

$= 8^2 - 4$

$= \ldots\ldots - 4$

$= \ldots\ldots$

**Hint**

Bracket first.

Indices next, $8^2 = 8 \times 8 = \ldots\ldots$

**Practice**

**3** Work out

**a** $3 + 3 \times 4$

$= \ldots\ldots$

$= \ldots\ldots$

**b** $(3 + 3) \times 4$

$= \ldots\ldots$

$= \ldots\ldots$

**c** $5 \times 3 + 5$

$= \ldots\ldots$

$= \ldots\ldots$

**d** $5 \times (3 + 5)$

$= \ldots\ldots$

$= \ldots\ldots$

**e** $20 - 5 \times 3$

$= \ldots\ldots$

$= \ldots\ldots$

**f** $(20 - 5) \times 3$

$= \ldots\ldots$

$= \ldots\ldots$

**g** $40 \div 5 - 3$

$= \ldots\ldots$

$= \ldots\ldots$

**h** $40 \div (5 - 3)$

$= \ldots\ldots$

$= \ldots\ldots$

**4** Work out

**a** $(10 + 6) \div (2 \times 4)$

$= \ldots\ldots$

$= \ldots\ldots$

$= \ldots\ldots$

**b** $10 + 6 \div 2 \times 4$

$= \ldots\ldots$

$= \ldots\ldots$

$= \ldots\ldots$

**c** $(5 + 2) \times (6 - 3)$

$= \ldots\ldots$

$= \ldots\ldots$

$= \ldots\ldots$

**d** $5 + 2 \times 6 - 3$

$= \ldots\ldots$

$= \ldots\ldots$

$= \ldots\ldots$

**e** $(3 + 7) \times (5 - 2)$    **f** $(3 + 7) \times 5 - 2$    **g** $3 + 7 \times (5 - 2)$    **h** $3 + 7 \times 5 - 2$

$= \dots$    $= \dots$    $= \dots$    $= \dots$

$= \dots$    $= \dots$    $= \dots$    $= \dots$

$= \dots$    $= \dots$    $= \dots$    $= \dots$

**5** Work out

**a** $2 \times (14 - 3^2)$    **b** $2 \times 14 - 3^2$    **c** $32 \div 2^2 + 12$    **d** $32 \div (2^2 + 12)$

$= \dots$    $= \dots$    $= \dots$    $= \dots$

$= \dots$    $= \dots$    $= \dots$    $= \dots$

$= \dots$    $= \dots$    $= \dots$    $= \dots$

**e** $6^2 \div 4 + 5 \times 3$    **f** $6^2 \div (4 + 5) \times 3$    **g** $48 \div 4 - 1 \times 2$    **h** $48 \div (4 - 1) \times 2$

$= \dots$    $= \dots$    $= \dots$    $= \dots$

$= \dots$    $= \dots$    $= \dots$    $= \dots$

$= \dots$    $= \dots$    $= \dots$    $= \dots$

**6** This table show the letters of the alphabet and the numbers 1 to 26.

| 1 | 2 | 3 | 4 | 5 | 6 | 7 | 8 | 9 | 10 | 11 | 12 | 13 | 14 | 15 | 16 | 17 | 18 | 19 | 20 | 21 | 22 | 23 | 24 | 25 | 26 |
|---|---|---|---|---|---|---|---|---|----|----|----|----|----|----|----|----|----|----|----|----|----|----|----|----|----|
| A | B | C | D | E | F | G | H | I | J | K | L | M | N | O | P | Q | R | S | T | U | V | W | X | Y | Z |

Work out the answers to these calculations. Then rearrange the letters to give the names of three English cities.

**a** $(9 + 7) \div 4 =$ ..................................................................

$5 + 3 \times 3 =$ ..................................................................

$3 \times 8 \div (10 - 8) =$ ..................................................................

$3 + 2 \times 6 =$ ..................................................................

$4^2 - (24 \div 12) =$ ..................................................................

$(8^2 - 4) \div (7 - 3) =$ ..................................................................

..................................................................

**b** $1 + 2 \times 7 =$ ..................................................................

$(4 \times 5) - (7 \div 7) =$ ..................................................................

$4^2 \div (3^2 - 1) =$ ..................................................................

$8 \times 6 \div 2^2 =$ ..................................................................

$(10 - 7) \times (1 + 2) =$ ..................................................................

$4 \times 6 - (5 - 1) =$ ..................................................................

$1 + 5 \times 4 - 3 =$ ..................................................................

..................................................................

**c** $2 \times 5 + 2^3 =$ ..................................................................

$(10 + 2) \div 3 =$ ..................................................................

$(8 - 3) \times (10 - 7) =$ ..................................................................

$100 \div 10 - (12 \div 3) =$ ..................................................................

$5^2 - 1 =$ ..................................................................

$8 \times 3 - 3^2 =$ ..................................................................

..................................................................

# Read, write and order decimals

## 3.1

By the end of this section you will know how to:

* Read, write, order and compare decimal numbers to two decimal places
* Understand place value in relation to decimal numbers

### Key points

* Place value is very important when comparing decimals with different numbers of digits after the decimal point.

* The first digit after the decimal point shows tenths and the second digit shows hundredths.

**Example**

**1** Write the decimal number shown in each grid.

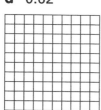   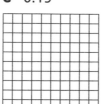   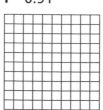

**Hint**

$\frac{1}{10} = 0.1$

$\frac{1}{100} = 0.01$

$\frac{32}{100} = 0.32$

**a** $\frac{5}{10} = 0.$......

**b** $\frac{......}{100} = 0.0$......

**c** $\frac{......}{10} + \frac{......}{100} =$ ..........

**Practice**

**2** Shade the grids to show the following decimal numbers.

**a** 0.7

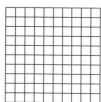

**b** 0.04

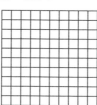

**c** 0.55

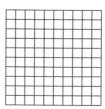

**d** 0.62

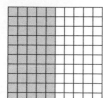

**e** 0.19

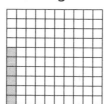

**f** 0.91

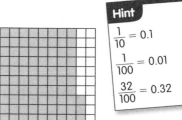

**Extend**

**3** Order the decimals in question 2, from smallest to largest. Use the grids to help you.

......................................................................................................

**Example**

**4** Write in missing zeros so the numbers have the same number of decimal places. Then write them in order, from smallest to largest.

**a**

| 0.56 | 0.5 | 0.65 | 0.7 | 0.6 | 0.76 |
|------|------|------|------|------|------|
| 0.56 | 0.50 | 0.65 | 0.70 | 0.60 | 0.76 |
| 2nd | 1st | 4th | 5th | 3rd | 6th |

0.5  0.56

**b**

| 2.5 | 2.35 | 2.4 | 2.53 | 2.19 |
|------|------|------|------|------|
| 2.50 | 2.35 | 2.40 | 2.53 | 2.19 |
| | | | | 1st |

2.19

**Practice**

**5** Order these decimals, starting with the smallest.

a    3.9    4.8    0.7    3.5    ..................................................

b    3.67    4.28    3.76    4.82    ..................................................

c    6.7    4.98    6.2    4.89    ..................................................

d    18.7    18.75    18.6    18.58    ..................................................

e    24.9    24.57    24.7    24.75    ..................................................

**6** Write these numbers in the correct place on the line:

5.5    6.5    7.5    5.1    6.8    7.3    6.3    7.9

5.8 has been done for you.

**7** Write these numbers in the correct place on the line:

5.1    5.2    5.4    5.6    5.7    5.9    5.15

5.25    5.45    5.75    5.85    5.68    5.33    5.99

**Extend**

**8** Write the names of the athletes to show the order in which they finished in their event. Include their times or distances.

| 100 m Sprint (seconds) | |
| --- | --- |
| B Blue | 15.65 |
| G Green | 15.7 |
| R Red | 15.56 |
| W White | 15.09 |

| Triple Jump (metres) | |
| --- | --- |
| T Highe | 16.07 |
| L Legge | 16.5 |
| B Speede | 16.49 |
| M Springer | 15.99 |

**Hint**

The winning time is the **shortest** time but the winning jump is the **longest** distance

a    100 m sprint:    ..................................................

b    Triple jump:    ..................................................

Need more practice ☐    Almost there ☐    Got it! ☐

# Add and subtract decimals

## 3.2

By the end of this section you will know how to:

* Add and subtract decimal numbers

**Key points**

* Place value is very important when adding and subtracting decimals.

* To add or subtract decimals, digits with the same place value should be lined up carefully, one under the other.

**Example**

1 **a** Add 3.4 and 5.8.

$$\begin{array}{r} 3.4 \\ + 5.8 \\ \hline \text{......} . 2 \\ \hline {\scriptstyle 1} \end{array}$$

**b** Total 5.38 and 3.92.

$$\begin{array}{r} 5.38 \\ + 3.92 \\ \hline \text{......} . \text{......} 0 \\ \hline {\scriptstyle 1} \quad {\scriptstyle 1} \end{array}$$

**c** Add 14.5 and 21.56.

$$\begin{array}{r} 21.56 \\ + 14.50 \\ \hline \text{..............} . \text{............} \end{array}$$

**Hint**

If you are adding numbers with different numbers of decimal places, make them the same by writing a zero in the empty place in the shorter number.

**Practice**

2 Work out the answers.

**a** 5.6 + 2.8

$$\begin{array}{r} 5.6 \\ + 2.8 \\ \hline \quad . \\ \hline \end{array}$$

**b** 4.68 + 2.37

$$\begin{array}{r} 4.68 \\ + 2.37 \\ \hline \quad . \\ \hline \end{array}$$

**c** 34.5 + 23.85

$$\begin{array}{r} 34.5 \\ + 23.85 \\ \hline \quad . \\ \hline \end{array}$$

**d** 3.9 + 2.5

**e** 7.29 + 3.04

**f** 37 + 58.93

**g** 4.6 + 5.92

**h** 47.37 + 25.8

**i** 6.84 + 48.5

**Extend**

3 **a** Work out the total of 24.6 and 52.73.

**b** How much altogether is 36.7 and 42.93?

**c** What is 3.46 + 12.7 + 5.08?

4 Use the fact that 275 + 629 = 904 to work out 27.5 + 62.9 = ......................................................................

**Example**

5 Work out the answers.

**a** 7.8 − 4.5

$$\begin{array}{r} 7.8 \\ - 4.5 \\ \hline \text{......} . 3 \\ \hline \end{array}$$

**b** 37.72 − 15.56

$$\begin{array}{r} 3\ 7.7\ {}^{1}2 \\ - 1\ 5.5\ 6 \\ \hline \text{..............} . \text{......} 6 \\ \hline \end{array}$$

**c** 7.3 − 5.18

$$\begin{array}{r} 7.3\ {}^{1}0 \\ - 5.1\ 8 \\ \hline \text{......} . \text{............} \\ \hline \end{array}$$

**Practice**

**6** Work out these decimal subtractions.

a  21.6 − 15.4

b  45.19 − 23.81

c  34.27 − 19.47

d  56.8 − 25.37

e  72.6 − 26.45

f  62.34 − 37.9

g  69.04 − 16.73

h  20.37 − 14.09

i  64.1 − 12.07

**Extend**

**7** a  How much more than 27.3 is 76.19?

..............................

b  What is the difference between 56.28 and 83.7?

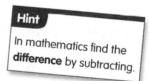

Hint

In mathematics find the **difference** by subtracting.

..............................

c  What is 5.67 + 14.93 − 8.6?

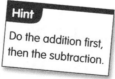

Hint

Do the addition first, then the subtraction.

..............................

**8** Find the pairs of numbers that add to 10.

| 2.75 | 6.5 | 6.8 | 7.3 |
|------|------|------|------|
| 0.75 | 3.65 | 3.15 | 4.5 |
| 3.2 | 2.7 | 7.25 | 9.25 |
| 6.85 | 5.5 | 6.35 | 3.5 |

.......... + .......... = 10       .......... + .......... = 10

.......... + .......... = 10       .......... + .......... = 10

.......... + .......... = 10       .......... + .......... = 10

.......... + .......... = 10       .......... + .......... = 10

# 3.3 Multiply and divide decimal numbers

By the end of this section you will know how to:

* Multiply and divide with decimal numbers
* Use a calculator to multiply and divide with decimals
* Multiply and divide numbers and decimals by 10 and 100

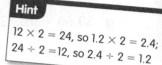

**Hint**

How to multiply and divide whole numbers by a single digit without a calculator.

**Key points**

* You can use whole number multiplication and division facts to multiply and divide with decimals.
* When multiplying or dividing by 10 or 100, the same rules apply to decimals and whole numbers.

**Hint**

$12 \times 2 = 24$, so $1.2 \times 2 = 2.4$;
$24 \div 2 = 12$, so $2.4 \div 2 = 1.2$

**Example**

**1** Use whole number calculations to work out the decimal multiplications.

**a** $15 \times 3 = 45$    so $1.5 \times 3 = \text{.........}$

**b** $24 \times 2 = 48$    so $2.4 \times \text{.........} = \text{.........}$

**c** $11 \times 5 = \text{.........}$    so $\text{.........} \times 5 = \text{.........}$

**d** $18 \times 4 = \text{.........}$    so $\text{.........} \times \text{.........} = \text{.........}$

**e** $132 \times 2 = \text{.........}$    so $13.2 \times 2 = \text{.........}$

**f** $243 \times 2 = \text{.........}$    so $\text{.........} \times 2 = \text{.........}$

**2** Use whole number calculations to work out the decimal divisions.

**a** $26 \div 2 = 13$    so $2.6 \div 2 = \text{.........}$

**b** $24 \div 3 = \text{.........}$    so $2.4 \div \text{.........} = 0.\text{.........}$

**c** $35 \div 5 = \text{.........}$    so $\text{.........} \div 5 = \text{.........}$

**d** $28 \div 4 = \text{.........}$    so $\text{.........} \div \text{.........} = \text{.........}$

**Practice**

**3** Use known number facts to work out these decimal calculations.

**a** $3.2 \div 8 = \text{.........}$    **b** $4.5 \div 9 = \text{.........}$    **c** $3.6 \div 4 = \text{.........}$

**d** $0.5 \times 3 = \text{.........}$    **e** $0.6 \times 4 = \text{.........}$    **f** $5 \times 0.4 = \text{.........}$

**g** $1.2 \times 3 = \text{.........}$    **h** $2.5 \times 3 = \text{.........}$    **i** $1.2 \div 3 = \text{.........}$

**4** Use a calculator to check what happens when you multiply decimals by 10 or 100.

**a** $7.6 \times 10 = \text{.........}$    **b** $8.3 \times 10 = \text{.........}$    **c** $45.6 \times 10 = \text{.........}$

**d** $36.7 \times 10 = \text{.........}$    **e** $3.5 \times 100 = \text{.........}$    **f** $6.8 \times 100 = \text{.........}$

**g** $37.4 \times 100 = \text{.........}$    **h** $74.6 \times 100 = \text{.........}$    **i** $2.59 \times 100 = \text{.........}$

**Hint**

Multiplying by 10 moves each digit one place to the left; multiplying by 100 moves each digit two places to the left.

**5** Look at the answers in question 4 to work out these calculations without a calculator.

**a** $3.2 \times 10 = \text{.........}$    **b** $6.9 \times 10 = \text{.........}$    **c** $57.5 \times 10 = \text{.........}$

**d** $5.7 \times 100 = \text{.........}$    **e** $8.2 \times 100 = \text{.........}$    **f** $52.8 \times 100 = \text{.........}$

**g** $34.8 \times 100 = \text{.........}$    **h** $3.48 \times 100 = \text{.........}$    **i** $7.89 \times 100 = \text{.........}$

**6** Use a calculator to check what happens when you divide whole numbers and decimals by 10 or 100.

   **a**  $36 \div 10 =$ ..........

   **b**  $72 \div 10 =$ ..........

   **c**  $15.4 \div 10 =$ ..........

   **d**  $28.3 \div 10 =$ ..........

   **e**  $5.6 \div 10 =$ ..........

   **f**  $4.8 \div 10 =$ ..........

   **g**  $27 \div 100 =$ ..........

   **h**  $93 \div 100 =$ ..........

   **i**  $123 \div 100 =$ ..........

   **j**  $456 \div 100 =$ ..........

   **k**  $6789 \div 100 =$ ..........

   **l**  $5432 \div 100 =$ ..........

**7** Look at the answers in question 6 to work out these calculations without a calculator.

   **a**  $49 \div 10 =$ ..........

   **b**  $84 \div 10 =$ ..........

   **c**  $17.6 \div 10 =$ ..........

   **d**  $37.4 \div 10 =$ ..........

   **e**  $4.8 \div 10 =$ ..........

   **f**  $8.9 \div 10 =$ ..........

   **g**  $36 \div 100 =$ ..........

   **h**  $72 \div 100 =$ ..........

   **i**  $468 \div 100 =$ ..........

   **j**  $752 \div 100 =$ ..........

   **k**  $3764 \div 100 =$ ..........

   **l**  $4821 \div 100 =$ ..........

> **Hint**
>
> Dividing by 10 moves each digit one place to the right; dividing by 100 moves each digit two places to the right.

**8** Use a calculator to find which answer belongs to which calculation.

   **a**  $17.08 \times 6 =$ ...............................................

   **b**  $567.25 \div 5 =$ ...............................................

   **c**  $443.1 \div 4.2 =$ ...............................................

   **d**  $9.23 \times 12.06 =$ ...............................................

> 113.45
> 102.48
> 111.3138
> 105.5

**Extend**

**9 a** Use the fact that $24 \times 8 = 192$ to work out $2.4 \times 8 =$ ..............

   **b** Use the fact that $192 \div 8 = 24$ to work out $19.2 \div 8 =$ ..............

   **c** Work out the answers.

   $1200 \div 1000 =$ ..............     $1.234 \times 1000 =$ ..............     $3.2 \times 6 =$ ..............

---

Need more practice ☐     Almost there ☐     Got it! ☐

# Rounding decimals

**3.4**

By the end of this section you will know how to:

* Round decimals to the nearest whole number
* Round decimals to one decimal place

> **Hint**
>
> 5 and above round up, 4 and below round down.

**Key points**

* The same rules of rounding apply to decimals and whole numbers.

* Round to the nearest whole number: round 0.1, 0.2, 0.3 and 0.4 down; round 0.5, 0.6, 0.7, 0.8 and 0.9 up.

* Round to the one decimal place: round down if the hundredths digit is 1, 2, 3 or 4; round up if it is 5, 6, 7, 8 or 9.

**21**

**Practice**

**1** Use the number line to help you to round these numbers to the nearest whole number.

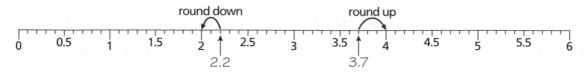

a 5.2 rounds to .........

b 5.8 rounds to .........

c 2.7 rounds to .........

d 3.4 rounds to .........

e 1.3 rounds to .........

f 4.5 rounds to .........

**2 a** Join each decimal to the nearest one decimal place. Use the number line to help.

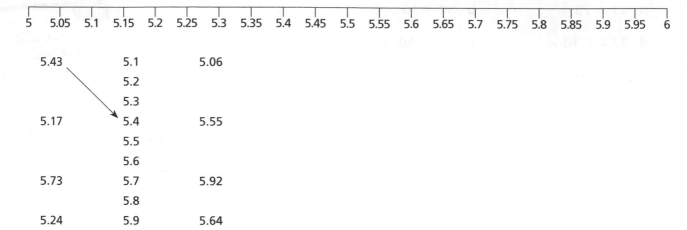

b Write each number correct to the nearest whole number.

45.62 ...............     45.263 ...............     45.3456 ...............

> **Hint**
>
> To round to the nearest whole number, look at the digit in the first decimal place. To round to one decimal place, look at the digit in the second decimal place.

c Write each number correct to one decimal place.

45.62 ...............     45.263 ...............     45.3456 ...............

**Extend**

**3 a** Write two decimal numbers that round up to 8. ...............

b Write two decimal numbers that round down to 8. ...............

c Write two decimal numbers that round up to 3.4 ...............

d Write two decimal numbers that round down to 3.4 ...............

e Write these decimals correct to one decimal place. 2.916 ......... 3.672 ......... 4.835 .........

f A number rounds up to 6, but down to 5.5. What number could it be? ...............

**Don't forget!**

✳ When you multiply a number by 10, each digit moves one place to the ...............................

✳ When you divide a number by 100, each digit moves ........................ to the ...........................

✳ What is wrong with this?

$$\begin{array}{r} 3\ 4\ .\ 5 \\ +\ 2\ .\ 5 \\ \hline 5\ 9\ .\ 5 \end{array}$$

..........................................................

..........................................................

**Unit test**

1  What is the value of the 6 in each of these numbers?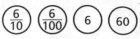

   **a**  34.67 ................................

   **b**  36.47 ................................

   **c**  34.76 ................................

2  Write these numbers in order of size. Start with the smallest number.

   34.7    34.67    36.47    34.76    36.04

   ..........................................................................................................

3  Round these numbers to the nearest whole number.

   **a**  24.67 ................................

   **b**  16.48 ................................

   **c**  29.706 ................................

4  Round these numbers correct to one decimal place.

   **a**  15.33 ................................

   **b**  36.47 ................................

   **c**  41.062 ................................

5  **a**  Work out   56.4 + 31.78

   **b**  Work out   65.4 − 31.78

   ...............................

   ...............................

6  Work out

   **a**  $0.5 \times 7 =$ ................................

   **b**  $5 \times 0.7 =$ ................................

   **c**  $3.5 \div 7 =$ ................................

   **d**  $2.4 \times 2 =$ ................................

   **e**  $4.2 \div 7 =$ ................................

   **f**  $4.6 \times 4 =$ ................................

7  Use your calculator to work out

   **a**  $17.09 \times 4.2$

   **b**  $67.48 \div 12.05$

   ...............................

   ...............................

8  **a**  Work out

   $24.05 \times 10 =$ ................................

   $2460 \div 10 =$ ................................

   $23\,900 \div 100 =$ ................................

   $2.45 \times 100 =$ ................................

   **b**  Write your answers to part **a** in order. Start with the smallest number.

   ..........................................................................................................

## Check solutions

**4.1**

By the end of this section you will know how to:

✳ Check calculations with an inverse operation
✳ Check calculations using approximation

**Key points**

✳ Use rounding to work out an approximate answer.

✳ Use inverse calculations and rounding to check answers.

**Hint**
Addition and subtraction are inverse operations. Multiplication and division are also inverse operations.

**Example**

**1** Write an inverse calculation to check these answers.

**a** $3 \times 4 = 12$        $12 \div 3 = $ .........

**b** $4 \times 9 = 36$        $36 \div $ ......... $= $ .........

**c** $24 \div 3 = 8$        ......... $\times$ ......... $= $ .........

**d** $54 \div 9 = 6$        ......... $\times$ ......... $= $ .........

**e** $34 + 56 = 90$        $90 - $ ......... $= $ .........

**f** $100 - 56 = $ .........        $56 + $ ......... $= $ .........

**2** Work out an approximate answer, using rounding to the nearest 10, 100 or 1. Then use a calculator to work out the actual answer. How close is your approximate answer?

**a** $48 + 52$    is about   $50 + 50 = $ .........        $48 + 52 = $ .........

**b** $121 - 59$        $120 - $ ......... $= $ .........        $121 - 59 = $ .........

**c** $618 - 498$        ......... $- $ ......... $= $ .........        $618 - 498 = $ .........

**d** $43 \times 59$        ......... $\times$ ......... $= $ .........        $43 \times 59 = $ .........

**e** $4.8 \times 3.9$        $5 \times $ ......... $= $ .........        $4.8 \times 3.9 = $ .........

**f** $25.6 \div 3.2$        ......... $\div$ ......... $= $ .........        $25.6 \div 3.2 = $ .........

**g** $3.2 + 5.8 + 6.7$        ......... $+$ ......... $+$ ......... $= $ .........        $3.2 + 5.8 + 6.7 = $ .........

**Practice**

**3** Use rounding to work out an approximate answer.
Use this to choose the correct answer to
these word problems from the numbers in the box.

| 51 | 82 | 216 | 270 | 494 |
|----|----|-----|-----|-----|

**a** Eggs are packed in trays of 18. How many eggs are in 12 trays?          .........

**b** £357 is shared equally between seven people. How much does each receive?          £ .........

**c** Two friends are sharing a prize of £988. How much do they each get?          £ .........

**d** There are 15 players in a rugby team. How many players are needed for 18 teams?          .........

**e** Queen Victoria was born in 1819 and died in 1901. How many years is this?          .........

**Extend**

**4  a** Estimate the answers.

  6.9 × 3.3 ⟶ ............................................                45.4 ÷ 8.7 ⟶ ............................................

  **b** A pair of trainers costs £59.95. Estimate the cost of 4 pairs of trainers.

  £ ............................

  **c** Eight boxes of printer paper cost £75. Estimate the cost of one box of printer paper.

  £ ............................

**5** Dave has calculated that the total of 14.56 and 23.7 is 38.26

  Choose the calculation you could use to check his answer.

  ☐ 23.7 − 38.26        ☐ 38.26 − 23.7        ☐ 38.26 + 14.56        ☐ 23.7 − 14.56

## Don't forget!

✳ To work out an approximate answer you need to ............................................................

✳ To check an answer you can use ............................................ or use ............................................

✳ Addition and ............................................ are inverse operations.

✳ Write two facts related to 5 × 6 = 30. ............................................ and ............................................

## Unit test

**1** Use rounding to work out an approximate answer to 21.09 × 3.9 ............... × ............... = ...............

**2** Use rounding to help to match the calculation to its approximate answer.

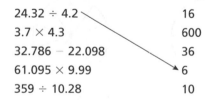

24.32 ÷ 4.2        16
3.7 × 4.3          600
32.786 − 22.098    36
61.095 × 9.99      6
359 ÷ 10.28        10

**3  a** Five pairs of socks cost £19.50. Estimate the cost of one pair of socks.

  £ ............................

  **b** One roll of ribbon costs £10.15. Estimate the cost of 8 rolls of ribbon.

  £ ............................

**4** Write a calculation you could use to check each answer.

  **a** 23.37 + 45.08 = 68.45  ............................................................

  **b** 34.4 × 21.5 = 739.6  ............................................................

  **c** 12.88 ÷ 5.6 = 2.3  ............................................................

# Read, write and order fractions

## 5.1

By the end of this section you will know how to:

* Read, write, order and compare fractions and mixed numbers

**Hint**

A **mixed number** is the same as a mixed fraction – it is a whole number with a fractional part, e.g. $3\frac{1}{2}$

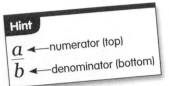

**Hint**

$\frac{a}{b}$ ← numerator (top)
← denominator (bottom)

### Key points

* As the denominator increases, the fractional part gets smaller.
* A fraction is part of a whole one.

**Example**

**1** Write the fraction that is shaded and the fraction that is **not** shaded.

**a** $\frac{1}{2}$ shaded      $\frac{1}{2}$ not shaded

**b** $\frac{\ }{4}$ shaded      .......... not shaded

**c** ......... shaded      ......... not shaded

**d** ......... shaded      ......... not shaded

**e** $1\frac{1}{4}$ shaded      ......... not shaded

**f** ......... shaded      ......... not shaded

**Practice**

**2** Shade the shapes to show these fractions.

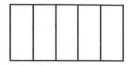 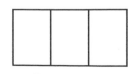 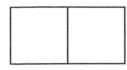 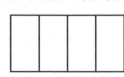 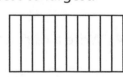

**a** $\frac{1}{5}$      **b** $\frac{1}{3}$      **c** $\frac{1}{2}$      **d** $\frac{1}{4}$      **e** $\frac{1}{10}$

**3** Use the shaded shapes in question 2 to write these fractions in order, starting with the smallest.

$\frac{1}{5}$      $\frac{1}{3}$      $\frac{1}{2}$      $\frac{1}{4}$      $\frac{1}{10}$

....................................................................................................

**4** Shade the shapes to show these fractions. Then write them in order from smallest to largest.

**a** $\frac{4}{5}$      **b** $\frac{2}{3}$      **c** $\frac{1}{2}$      **d** $\frac{3}{4}$      **e** $\frac{9}{10}$

**Extend**

**5** Using what you learned in questions 2 and 4, write these fractions in order. Start with the smallest.

a  $\frac{1}{3}$    $\frac{1}{7}$    $\frac{1}{5}$    $\frac{1}{2}$    $\frac{1}{4}$    $\frac{1}{6}$    ...........................................................................

b  $\frac{9}{10}$    $\frac{5}{6}$    $\frac{11}{12}$    $\frac{2}{3}$    $\frac{7}{8}$    $\frac{4}{5}$    ...........................................................................

**6** Continue the pattern of fractions. Write the next three numbers in each pattern.

a  $\frac{1}{2}$    1    $1\frac{1}{2}$    2    $2\frac{1}{2}$    3    ...........................................................................

b  $\frac{1}{4}$    $\frac{2}{4}$    $\frac{3}{4}$    1    $1\frac{1}{4}$    $1\frac{2}{4}$    ...........................................................................

c  $\frac{1}{2}$    $\frac{1}{3}$    $\frac{1}{4}$    $\frac{1}{5}$    ...........................................................................

d  $\frac{1}{2}$    $\frac{2}{3}$    $\frac{3}{4}$    $\frac{4}{5}$    ...........................................................................

Need more practice ☐    Almost there ☐    Got it! ☐

# Use equivalent fractions

## 5.2

By the end of this section you will know how to:

✳ Identify equivalent fractions

### Key points

✳ **Equivalent** means equal.

✳ Any fraction has many equivalent fractions.

**Example**

**1** These pairs of fractions are equivalent. Write the equivalent fractions.

a

$$\frac{1}{2} = \frac{2}{.....}$$

b

$$\frac{3}{4} = \frac{.....}{.....}$$

c

$$..........  =  ..........$$

d

$$..........  =  ..........$$

**Practice**

**2** Use the fraction board to identify some more equivalent fractions.

a  $\frac{1}{2} = \frac{.....}{4} = \frac{.....}{6} = \frac{.....}{10}$    b  $\frac{1}{3} = \frac{.....}{6}$    c  $\frac{2}{5} = \frac{.....}{10}$

d  $\frac{3}{4} = \frac{.....}{8}$    e  $\frac{2}{3} = \frac{.....}{6}$    f  $\frac{8}{10} = \frac{.....}{5}$

g  $\frac{2}{6} = \frac{1}{.....}$    h  $\frac{6}{10} = \frac{3}{.....}$    i  $\frac{2}{4} = \frac{4}{.....}$

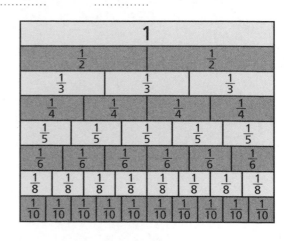

| 1 | | | | | | | | | |
|---|---|---|---|---|---|---|---|---|---|
| $\frac{1}{2}$ | | | | | $\frac{1}{2}$ | | | | |
| $\frac{1}{3}$ | | | $\frac{1}{3}$ | | | | $\frac{1}{3}$ | | |
| $\frac{1}{4}$ | | $\frac{1}{4}$ | | $\frac{1}{4}$ | | | $\frac{1}{4}$ | | |
| $\frac{1}{5}$ | | $\frac{1}{5}$ | $\frac{1}{5}$ | | $\frac{1}{5}$ | | $\frac{1}{5}$ | | |
| $\frac{1}{6}$ | $\frac{1}{6}$ | | $\frac{1}{6}$ | $\frac{1}{6}$ | | $\frac{1}{6}$ | | $\frac{1}{6}$ | |
| $\frac{1}{8}$ | $\frac{1}{8}$ | $\frac{1}{8}$ | $\frac{1}{8}$ | $\frac{1}{8}$ | $\frac{1}{8}$ | $\frac{1}{8}$ | $\frac{1}{8}$ | | |
| $\frac{1}{10}$ | $\frac{1}{10}$ | $\frac{1}{10}$ | $\frac{1}{10}$ | $\frac{1}{10}$ | $\frac{1}{10}$ | $\frac{1}{10}$ | $\frac{1}{10}$ | $\frac{1}{10}$ | $\frac{1}{10}$ |

**Example**

3 Complete these sets of equivalent fractions.

a $\frac{1}{2} \overset{\times 2}{\underset{\times 2}{=}} \frac{2}{4} \overset{\times 2}{\underset{\times 2 \ldots}{=}} \frac{4}{\ldots} \overset{\times 2}{\underset{\times 2}{=}} \frac{\ldots}{16}$

b $\frac{2}{3} \overset{\times 10}{\underset{\times 10 \ldots}{=}} \frac{20}{\ldots}$

c $\frac{3}{10} \overset{\times 3}{\underset{\times 3 \ldots}{=}} \frac{\ldots}{\ldots}$

> **Hint**
> You can make equivalent fractions by multiplying both parts of a fraction by the same number.

**Practice**

4 Write equivalent fractions for these fractions.

a $\frac{3}{4} = \frac{\ldots}{\ldots} = \frac{\ldots}{\ldots}$

b $\frac{5}{8} = \frac{\ldots}{\ldots} = \frac{\ldots}{\ldots}$

c $\frac{4}{5} = \frac{\ldots}{\ldots} = \frac{\ldots}{\ldots}$

---

Need more practice ☐   Almost there ☐   Got it! ☐

# 5.3 Write fractions in their simplest form

By the end of this section you will know how to:

* Simplify (cancel down) fractions

> **Hint**
> The factors of a number have that number in their times tables.

**Key points**

* **Simplifying** is the opposite of finding equivalent fractions by multiplying.

* Fractions are **simplified** by dividing the numerator and the denominator by the same number.

* A fraction is in its **simplest form** when you can't divide the numerator and denominator any further.

**Example**

1 Write these fractions as simply as possible.

a

$\frac{2}{8} = \frac{1}{\ldots}$

b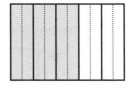

$\frac{6}{10} = \frac{\ldots}{\ldots}$

c

$\frac{\ldots}{\ldots} = \frac{\ldots}{\ldots}$

d

$\frac{\ldots}{\ldots} = \frac{\ldots}{\ldots}$

e

$\frac{\ldots}{\ldots} = \frac{\ldots}{\ldots}$

f

$\frac{\ldots}{\ldots} = \frac{\ldots}{\ldots}$

**Practice**

2 Simplify these fractions.

a $\frac{5}{10} \overset{\div 5}{\underset{\div 5 \ldots}{=}} \frac{\ldots}{\ldots}$

b $\frac{14}{20} \overset{\div 2}{\underset{\div 2 \ldots}{=}} \frac{\ldots}{\ldots}$

c $\frac{12}{15} \overset{\div 3}{\underset{\div 3 \ldots}{=}} \frac{\ldots}{\ldots}$

> **Hint**
> Simplify fractions by dividing both parts of the fraction by the same number.

d $\frac{6}{12} = \frac{\ldots}{\ldots}$

e $\frac{15}{20} = \frac{\ldots}{\ldots}$

f $\frac{12}{16} = \frac{\ldots}{\ldots}$

**Extend**

**3** Join the pairs of equivalent fractions

$\frac{2}{3}$    $\frac{10}{20}$    $\frac{4}{5}$    $\frac{6}{9}$    $\frac{8}{10}$    $\frac{3}{4}$    $\frac{1}{2}$    $\frac{1}{4}$    $\frac{6}{8}$    $\frac{4}{16}$

Need more practice ☐    Almost there ☐    Got it! ☐

## 5.4 Convert between fractions and decimals

By the end of this section you will know how to:

* Convert simple fractions to decimals
* Convert simple decimals to fractions

### Key points

* All fractions have a decimal equivalent.
* All decimals have a fraction equivalent.

**Example**

**1 a** Choose the decimals and fractions from this box to complete the two number lines.

| 0.5 | $\frac{1}{4}$ | 0.75 | $\frac{3}{4}$ | 0.25 | $\frac{1}{2}$ |

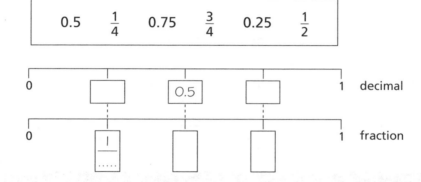

**b** Use the number lines to find the pairs of equivalent fractions and decimals.

$\frac{1}{4} = 0.\underline{\quad}$        $\frac{1}{2} = \underline{\quad}$        $\frac{\underline{\quad}}{\underline{\quad}} = \underline{\quad}$

**Practice**

**2 a** Complete both number lines.

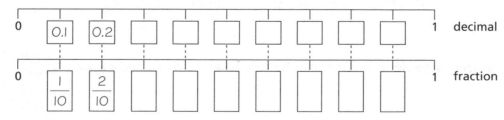

**b** Use the completed number lines to write the equivalent fractions and decimals.

$0.1 = \frac{\underline{\quad}}{\underline{\quad}}$        $\frac{2}{10} = \underline{\quad}$        $0.4 = \frac{\underline{\quad}}{\underline{\quad}}$        $\frac{9}{10} = \underline{\quad}$

**Example**

3  Use a calculator to change these fractions into decimals.

a  $\frac{1}{5} = 1 \div 5 = 0.\underline{\hspace{1cm}}$

b  $\frac{3}{5} = 3 \div 5 = \underline{\hspace{1cm}}$

c  $\frac{4}{5} = \underline{\hspace{0.8cm}} \div \underline{\hspace{0.8cm}} = \underline{\hspace{0.8cm}}$

d  $\frac{1}{20} = \underline{\hspace{0.8cm}} \div \underline{\hspace{0.8cm}} = \underline{\hspace{0.8cm}}$

e  $\frac{3}{20} = \underline{\hspace{2cm}}$

f  $\frac{21}{25} = \underline{\hspace{2cm}}$

**Extend**

4  Convert the fractions into decimals. Then write them in order, starting with the smallest.

| Fraction | $\frac{3}{4}$ | $\frac{2}{5}$ | $\frac{5}{8}$ | $\frac{12}{15}$ | $\frac{9}{20}$ |
|---|---|---|---|---|---|
| Decimal | | | | | |

Order  _____

## Convert decimals into fractions

**Hint**

0.5 means 5 tenths $= \frac{5}{10}$

0.45 means 45 hundredths $= \frac{45}{100}$

**Example**

5  Change these decimals into a fraction in tenths or hundredths. Then simplify where possible.

a  $0.8 = \frac{8}{10}\begin{smallmatrix}\div 2 \\ \\ \div 2\end{smallmatrix} = \underline{\cdots}$

b  $0.7 = \frac{\cdots}{\cdots}$

c  $0.4 = \frac{\cdots}{\cdots} = \frac{\cdots}{\cdots}$

d  $0.15 = \frac{15}{100}\begin{smallmatrix}\div 5 \\ \\ \div 5\end{smallmatrix} = \underline{\cdots}$

e  $0.19 = \frac{\cdots}{\cdots}$

f  $0.28 = \frac{\cdots}{\cdots}\begin{smallmatrix}\div 4 \\ \\ \div 4\end{smallmatrix} = \frac{\cdots}{\cdots}$

**Extend**

6  Complete the table to show the equivalent fractions and decimals.

| Decimal | 0.5 | | 0.9 | | 0.2 | |
|---|---|---|---|---|---|---|
| Fraction | | $\frac{3}{4}$ | | $\frac{11}{100}$ | | $\frac{3}{10}$ |

Need more practice ☐     Almost there ☐     Got it! ☐

# Add and subtract fractions

**5.5**

By the end of this section you will know how to:

* Add and subtract fractions with the same denominator

## Key points

* Fractions with the same denominator can be added and subtracted easily.

**Hint**

How to read a shaded diagram showing a fraction.

**Example**

1  Show these fraction diagrams as an addition.

a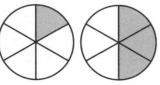

b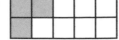

c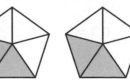

$\frac{1}{6} + \frac{3}{6} = \frac{\cdots}{6}$

$\frac{3}{10} + \frac{\cdots}{\cdots} = \frac{\cdots}{\cdots}$

$\frac{\cdots}{\cdots} + \frac{\cdots}{\cdots} = \frac{\cdots}{\cdots}$

**Practice**

**2** Add these fractions. Simplify your answers where possible.

**a** $\frac{1}{5} + \frac{3}{5} = \frac{\ \ }{\ \ }$

**b** $\frac{5}{10} + \frac{3}{10} = \frac{\ \ }{\ \ } = \frac{\ \ }{\ \ }$

**c** $\frac{1}{8} + \frac{5}{8} = \frac{\ \ }{\ \ } = \frac{\ \ }{\ \ }$

**3** Subtract these fractions. Simplify your answers where possible.

   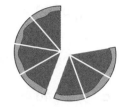

**a** $\frac{4}{5} - \frac{1}{5} = \frac{\ \ }{\ \ }$

**b** $\frac{7}{10} - \frac{2}{10} = \frac{\ \ }{\ \ } = \frac{\ \ }{\ \ }$

**c** $\frac{5}{6} - \frac{2}{6} = \frac{\ \ }{\ \ } = \frac{\ \ }{\ \ }$

**d** $\frac{7}{9} - \frac{3}{9} = \frac{\ \ }{\ \ }$

**Extend**

**4** Work out the answers. Write the fraction in its simplest form.

**a** $\frac{7}{12} + \frac{3}{12} =$ ..................................................

**b** $\frac{7}{12} - \frac{3}{12} =$ ..................................................

**c** $\frac{4}{9} + \frac{4}{9} =$ ..................................................

**d** $\frac{6}{11} - \frac{5}{11} =$ ..................................................

---

Need more practice ☐      Almost there ☐      Got it! ☐

# Find fractions of quantities

By the end of this section you will know how to:

* Find a fraction of a quantity
* Multiply a fraction by a positive integer

**Key points**

* To multiply a fraction, multiply the numerator.
* To find a fraction of a number, divide by the denominator.

> **Hint**
> A fraction is a way of showing division, e.g. $\frac{3}{10} = 3 \div 10$.

**Example**

**1** Write these as multiplications to find the answer.

**a**

**b**

**c**

> **Hint**
> Related division facts for 2, 3, 4, 5 and 10 times tables.

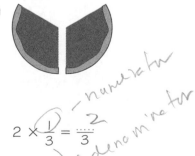

$2 \times \frac{1}{3} = \frac{2}{3}$

$3 \times \frac{\ \ }{10} = \frac{\ \ }{\ \ } = \frac{\ \ }{\ \ }$

$\ldots \ldots \times \frac{\ \ }{5} = \frac{\ \ }{\ \ }$

**Practice**

**2** Work out these multiplications. Simplify where possible.

**a** $3 \times \frac{1}{8} =$ ..................

**b** $4 \times \frac{1}{7} =$ ..................

**c** $2 \times \frac{3}{10} =$ ..................

**d** $3 \times \frac{4}{20} =$ ..................

**e** $\frac{4}{15} \times 2 =$ ..................

**f** $\frac{2}{11} \times 5 =$ ..................

**g** $\frac{3}{7} \times 2 =$ ..................

**h** $5 \times \frac{3}{20} =$ ..................

**i** $\frac{2}{9} \times 3 =$ ..................

**3** Find the fraction of the number using division.

**a** $\frac{1}{2}$ of 16 = 16 ÷ 2 = .........

**b** $\frac{1}{3}$ of 12 = 12 ÷ ......... = .........

**c** $\frac{1}{5}$ of 20 = ......... ÷ ......... = .........

**d** $\frac{1}{4}$ of 20 = ......... ......... = .........

**e** $\frac{1}{10}$ of 20 = ......... ......... = .........

**f** $\frac{1}{3}$ of 18 = ......... ......... = .........

> **Hint**
>
> To find $\frac{1}{2}$ divide by **2**; to find $\frac{1}{4}$ divide by **4**.

**4** Find the fraction of the number using division.

**a** $\frac{1}{10}$ of 40 = .....................

**b** $\frac{1}{5}$ of 25 = .....................

**c** $\frac{1}{6}$ of 30 = .....................

**d** $\frac{1}{9}$ of 27 = .....................

**e** $\frac{1}{8}$ of 32 = .....................

**f** $\frac{1}{7}$ of 28 = .....................

**5 a** Find $\frac{1}{5}$ of these apples, by dividing them into the five crates.

**b** Find these fractions.

$\frac{1}{5}$ of 30 = 30 ÷ ......... = .........

$\frac{2}{5}$ of 30 = $\frac{1}{5}$ of 30 × 2 = 30 ÷ 5 × 2 = ......... × 2 = .........

$\frac{3}{5}$ of 30 = ......... × 3 = .........

$\frac{4}{5}$ of 30 = ......... × ......... = .........

> **Hint**
>
> To find $\frac{3}{5}$ of a number, find $\frac{1}{5}$ by dividing by **5**, then multiply by **3** to find $\frac{3}{5}$.

**6** Use division then multiplication to find these fractions.

**a** $\frac{3}{4}$ of 20 = .....................

**b** $\frac{7}{10}$ of 40 = .....................

**c** $\frac{4}{5}$ of 50 = .....................

**d** $\frac{3}{8}$ of 24 = .....................

**e** $\frac{3}{10}$ of 60 = .....................

**f** $\frac{2}{3}$ of 30 = .....................

**7** Work out the answers.

**a** $\frac{3}{4}$ of 60 = .....................

**b** $\frac{3}{5}$ of 150 = .....................

**c** $\frac{5}{6}$ of 120 = .....................

**d** $\frac{9}{10}$ of 450 = .....................

**e** $\frac{4}{11}$ of 66 = .....................

**f** $\frac{4}{9}$ of 72 = .....................

## Don't forget!

 Shade each shape to show the fraction.

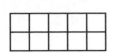

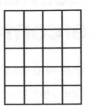

a $\frac{3}{5}$

b $\frac{5}{6}$

c $\frac{3}{10}$

 Match the equivalent fractions.

$\frac{3}{4}$     $\frac{2}{3}$     $\frac{1}{2}$     $\frac{1}{4}$

$\frac{15}{30}$     $\frac{15}{20}$     $\frac{5}{20}$     $\frac{20}{30}$

* Fill in the table of equivalent fractions and decimals.

| Decimal | | 0.5 | | 0.01 | | 0.17 |
|---|---|---|---|---|---|---|
| Fraction | $\frac{1}{10}$ | | $\frac{9}{10}$ | | $\frac{4}{100}$ | |

* To change a decimal into a fraction you ............................................................................................,

then ........................... the fraction if you can.

* To find $\frac{1}{5}$ of a quantity you ...............................................................

* To find $\frac{3}{4}$ of a quantity you ................................................ then ...............................................

## Unit test

1 a Work out $\frac{3}{7} + \frac{2}{7}$ ........................     b Work out $\frac{7}{8} - \frac{5}{8}$ ........................

2 a Work out $\frac{1}{5}$ of 35 ........................     b Work out $\frac{1}{4}$ of 24 ........................

3 a Work out $\frac{3}{4}$ of 32 ........................     b Work out $\frac{3}{10}$ of 40 ........................

4 a Find an equivalent fraction to $\frac{10}{20}$ .........     b Write $\frac{8}{10}$ in its simplest form. ........................

5 a Write 0.7 as a fraction. ........................     b Write $\frac{1}{4}$ as a decimal. ........................

6 Work out $\frac{1}{4}$ of £40.     £ ........................

7 Write these fractions in order of size. Start with the smallest fraction.

$\frac{1}{4}$     $\frac{3}{4}$     $\frac{1}{2}$     $\frac{1}{5}$ ........................................................................

## 6.1 Decimals, fractions and percentages

By the end of this section you will know how to:

* Convert some decimals and fractions into percentages
* Convert percentages into decimals and fractions

### Key points

* Percentage means out of 100.

* 100% means $\frac{100}{100}$, all, the whole, everything.

* All percentages have a decimal and a fraction equivalent.

**Practice**

**1** Colour the grids to show the percentages.

**a** 50%    **b** 85%    **c** 23%

**Example**

**2** Complete these number lines.

**a**

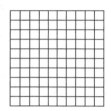 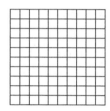 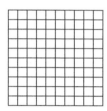

| 0 | ☐ | 0.5 | ☐ | 1 | decimal |

| 0 | $\frac{1}{4}$ | ☐ | ☐ | 1 | fraction |

| 0% | ☐ | ☐ | 75% | 100% | percentage |

**Hint**

The decimal equivalents for quarters and tenths.
The fraction equivalents for 0.25, 0.5, 0.75 and all tenths.

**b**

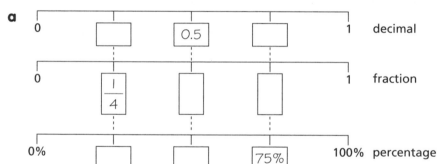

| 0 | 0.1 | ☐ ☐ ☐ ☐ ☐ ☐ ☐ ☐ | 1 | decimal |

| 0 | ☐ ☐ $\frac{3}{10}$ ☐ ☐ ☐ ☐ ☐ ☐ | 1 | fraction |

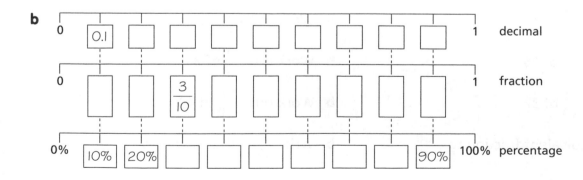

| 0% | 10% | 20% | ☐ ☐ ☐ ☐ ☐ ☐ | 90% | 100% | percentage |

**Practice**

**3** Use the number lines to complete these equivalent fractions, decimals and percentages.

**a** 0.5 = ........ % = ........

**b** 25% = ........ = ........

**c** $\frac{3}{4}$ = ........ % = ........

**d** 0.1 = ........ % = ........

**e** 20% = ........ = ........

**f** $\frac{7}{10}$ = ........ % = ........

**Extend**

**4** Complete the table to show the equivalent decimals, fractions and percentages.

| Fraction | Decimal | Percentage |
|---|---|---|
| $\frac{3}{10}$ | | |
| | 0.25 | |
| | | 90% |
| $\frac{4}{10}$ | | |
| | 0.8 | |
| | | 75% |

**Example**

**5** Convert each fraction into an equivalent decimal, then write the equivalent percentage.

Divide fraction (decimal)                 × 100 (percentage)

**a** $\frac{1}{5} = 1 \div 5 = 0.2$          $0.2 \times 100 = \underline{\quad} \%$

**b** $\frac{3}{5} = 3 \div 5 = \underline{\quad}$          $\underline{\quad} \times 100 = \underline{\quad} \%$

**c** $\frac{1}{20} = \underline{\quad} = \underline{\quad}$          $\underline{\quad} \times \underline{\quad} = \underline{\quad} \%$

**6** Convert each percentage into a decimal by dividing by 100.

**a** $45\% \overset{\div 100}{=} 0.\underline{\quad}$          **b** $40\% = 0.\underline{\quad}$          **c** $4\% = 0.\underline{\quad}$

**Hint**

How to divide a 2-digit number by 100.

**7** Convert each percentage into a fraction, simplifying where you can.

**a** $20\% = \frac{20}{100} \overset{\div 10}{\underset{\div 10}{=}} \frac{2}{10} \overset{\div 2}{\underset{\div 2}{=}} \frac{\underline{\quad}}{\underline{\quad}}$          **b** $11\% = \frac{\underline{\quad}}{100}$          **c** $9\% = \frac{9}{\underline{\quad}}$

**Practice**

**8 a** Convert these fractions into percentages.

$\frac{11}{20} = \underline{\hspace{4cm}}$          $\frac{15}{20} = \underline{\hspace{4cm}}$

$\frac{1}{8} = \underline{\hspace{4cm}}$          $\frac{3}{8} = \underline{\hspace{4cm}}$

**b** Convert these percentages into decimals.

$35\% = \underline{\hspace{2.5cm}}$          $80\% = \underline{\hspace{2.5cm}}$          $8\% = \underline{\hspace{2.5cm}}$

$15\% = \underline{\hspace{2.5cm}}$          $30\% = \underline{\hspace{2.5cm}}$          $9\% = \underline{\hspace{2.5cm}}$

**c** Convert these percentages into fractions, simplifying where possible.

$30\% = \underline{\hspace{2.5cm}}$          $29\% = \underline{\hspace{2.5cm}}$          $3\% = \underline{\hspace{2.5cm}}$

$35\% = \underline{\hspace{2.5cm}}$          $80\% = \underline{\hspace{2.5cm}}$          $22\% = \underline{\hspace{2.5cm}}$

**Extend**

**9** Find the sets of three equivalents – a decimal, a fraction and percentage. Record them in the table.

0.7   40%   $\frac{7}{10}$   0.17

0.75   50%   $\frac{15}{20}$   0.5

$\frac{2}{5}$   75%   0.4   $\frac{20}{40}$

$\frac{17}{100}$   70%   17%

| Fraction | Decimal | Percentage |
|----------|---------|------------|
|          |         |            |
|          |         |            |
|          |         |            |
|          |         |            |
|          |         |            |

Need more practice ☐   Almost there ☐   Got it! ☐

# Order and compare percentages

**6.2**

By the end of this section you will know how to:
* Order and compare percentages of amounts
* Use the equivalence of fractions, decimals and percentages

## Key points

* Equivalence can be used to order fractions, decimals and percentages.

**Example**

**1** Change the fractions and decimals into percentages to order them. Start with the smallest.

a  0.35   25%   $\frac{3}{10}$

35%   25%   30%

25%   $\frac{3}{10}$   .........

b  0.89   $\frac{9}{10}$   87%

89%   .........%   .........

87%   .........   .........

c  $\frac{3}{5}$   0.59   63%

60 .....   .........   .........

.........   .........   .........

**Practice**

**2** Write these fractions, decimals and percentages in order. Start with the smallest.

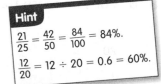

> **Hint**
> $\frac{21}{25} = \frac{42}{50} = \frac{84}{100} = 84\%$.
> $\frac{12}{20} = 12 \div 20 = 0.6 = 60\%$.

a   0.7   $\frac{3}{4}$   74%   ...................................

b   $\frac{1}{5}$   21%   0.19   ...................................

c   0.72   65%   $\frac{7}{10}$   ...................................

d   0.81   78%   $\frac{4}{5}$   ...................................

e   $\frac{1}{10}$   0.12   9%   ...................................

f   17%   0.2   $\frac{3}{20}$      ...................................

g   0.5   $\frac{11}{20}$   53%      ...................................

h   $\frac{5}{8}$   49%   0.6      ...................................

i   $\frac{21}{25}$   0.85   83%      ...................................

**36**

**Extend**

**3 a** Change these scores into percentages using a calculator or by changing the fractions to hundredths.

Maths $\frac{77}{100}$   $\frac{77}{100} = \text{.............}$ %

English $\frac{36}{50}$   $\frac{36}{50} = \frac{}{100} = \text{.............}$ %

Science $\frac{21}{25}$   $\frac{21}{25} = \frac{}{50} = \frac{}{100} = \text{.............}$ %

Art $\frac{7}{10}$   $\frac{7}{10} = \frac{}{100} = \text{.............}$ %

RE $\frac{16}{20}$   $\frac{16}{20} = \frac{}{10} = \frac{}{100} = \text{.............}$ %

**b** Write the subjects in order, starting with the best test score.

Need more practice ☐   Almost there ☐   Got it! ☐

# Find percentages of quantities

## 6.3

By the end of this section you will know how to:

★ Find 10%, 20%, 5% and 15% of a quantity mentally and with a calculator

★ Find 25%, 50% and 75% of a quantity mentally and with a calculator

★ Work out VAT payable

★ Order percentages of quantities

### Key points

★ $10\% = \frac{1}{10}$

★ 5% is half of 10%.

★ 20% is double 10%.

★ 15% is 10% + 5%.

★ A 2-digit percentage of a number is always less than the number.

**Hint**
$10\% = \frac{1}{10}$ so to find 10%, divide by 10.

### Find 10%, 20%, 5% and 15% of quantities

**Hint**
How to divide any number by 10.

**Example**

**1** Find 10% of these amounts by dividing by 10.

**a** 10% of £300 = 300 ÷ 10 = £ .............

**b** 10% of £65 = 65 ÷ 10 = ......... = £6.50

**c** 10% of £124 = ....... ÷ ....... = 12. ....... = £ .............

**d** 10% of £388 = .....................................

**Practice**

**2** Find 10% of these amounts – remember to write the unit of measure.

**a** 10% of £60 = .............

**b** 10% of £56 = .............

**c** 10% of £286 = .............

**d** 10% of 620 g = .............

**e** 10% of 3400 ml = .............

**f** 10% of 450 cm = .............

**g** 10% of 700 km = .............

**h** 10% of 3500 g = .............

**i** 10% of £4000 = .............

**Example**

**3** Find 20% by doubling 10% and find 5% by halving 10%.

**a** 20% of £30 = (10% of 30) × 2 = 3 × 2 = ............    20% of £30 = £ ............

**b** 5% of £400 = (10% of 400) ÷ 2 = 40 ÷ 2 = ............    5% of £400 = £ ............

**c** 20% of £75 = (10% of 75) × 2 = ............    20% of £75 = £ ............

**d** 5% of £60 = (10% of ............) ÷ ............ = ............    5% of £60 = £ ............

**e** 20% of £140 = ............................................    20% of £140 = £ ............

**f** 5% of £120 = ............................................    5% of £120 = £ ............

**Practice**

**4** Find 15% by finding 10% and 5% and adding.

| Amount | 10% | 5% | 10% + 5% | 15% of amount |
|--------|-----|-----|----------|---------------|
| £60 | | | | 15% of £60 = |
| £100 | | | | 15% of £100 = |
| £120 | | | | 15% of £120 = |
| £360 | | | | 15% of £360 = |
| £240 | | | | 15% of £240 = |
| £500 | | | | 15% of £500 = |

**5** Work out these percentages.

**a** 10% of £45

**b** 20% of £50

**c** 5% of £160

**d** 15% of £80

**e** 10% of £15

**f** 20% of £70

**g** 5% of £440

**h** 15% of £320

**i** 20% of £150

**j** 10% of £648

**k** 20% of £420

**l** 15% of £1000

**6** Work out which pairs of percentages have the same answer. Then complete the statements.

| 50% of £50 | 25% of £120 | 10% of £300 | 20% of £100 | 10% of £250 | 5% of £400 |

50% of £50 = ............................................ = ............

............................................ = ............................................ = ............

............................................ = ............................................ = ............

**Extend**

**7** Work out the answers.

  **a** Work out 5% of £70.

  **b** Work out 15% of £70.

  **c** Work out 30% of £40.

  .............................................          .............................................          .............................................

  **d** 54% of a school are boys. What percentage are girls?          .............................................

  **e** 10% of a number is 8. What is the number?          .............................................

## Find 25%, 50%, and 75% of quantities

**Practice**

**8 a** Write $\frac{1}{2}$ as a percentage. .............................................

  **b** Write 25% as a fraction. .............................................

**Example**

**9** Work out these percentages

  **a** 50% of £120 = 120 ÷ 2 = £.............

  **b** 25% of £120 = 120 ÷ 4 = £.............

  **c** 25% of £80 = 80 ÷ ............. = £.............

  **d** 50% of £80 = ............. ÷ ............. = £.............

  **e** 75% of £120 = 50% of 120 + ............. of 120 = ............. + ............. = £.............

  **f** 75% of £80 = ............................. + ............................. = ............. + ............. = £.............

**Practice**

**10** Work out these percentages of £180.

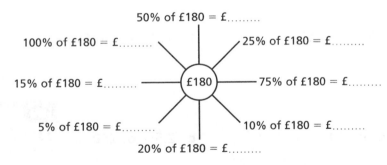

50% of £180 = £.........

100% of £180 = £.........          25% of £180 = £.........

15% of £180 = £.........          £180          75% of £180 = £.........

5% of £180 = £.........          10% of £180 = £.........

20% of £180 = £.........

**Example**

**11** Work out these percentages.

  **a** 25% of 364 = 364 × 25 ÷ 100 = £.............

  **b** 75% of £440 = 440 × ......... ÷ ......... = £.............

  **c** 85% of £360 = ......... × ......... ÷ ......... = £.............

  **d** 42% of £450 = ......... × ......... ÷ ......... = £.............

**Extend**

**12 a** A dress costs £64. The price is reduced by 50%. What is the new price?

£ .........................................

**b** Which is better value? Show your working out.

$\frac{2}{5}$ OFF          25% reduction

.........................................

**13** Shade 25% of these diagrams.

**a**

**b**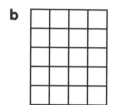

**c**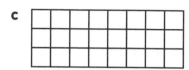

## Value added tax (VAT)

**Example**

**14** VAT of 20% is charged on these amounts. Find the amount of VAT charged.

**a** £50: 20% VAT = £50 ÷ 10 × 2 = £ ............

**b** £90: 20% VAT = £90 ÷ ........ × ........ = £ ............

**c** £45: 20% VAT = ........ ÷ ........ × ........ = £ ............

**d** £75: 20% VAT = .........................................

**Practice**

**15** Work out the tax on goods that cost these amounts.

**a** 15% tax on £50

**b** 25% tax on £60

**c** 10% tax on £75

.........................................

.........................................

.........................................

**d** 20% tax on £35

**e** 20% tax on £125

**f** 15% tax on £150

.........................................

.........................................

.........................................

**16** Work out

**a** 10% of £80

**b** 5% of £80

**c** 2.5% of £80

.........................................

.........................................

.........................................

**d** Use your answers to **a**, **b** and **c** to work out 17.5% of £80.

£ .........................................

**Extend**

**17** A bill was £110 plus VAT at 20%. Complete the bill below.

| Bill | |
|---|---|
| Cost of work | £110.00 |
| + VAT at 20% | £ ............................ |
| Total | £ ............................ |

## Don't forget!

* Match the statements that mean the same.

100%          $\frac{1}{2}$ price          save 25%

| 50% off |   | $\frac{1}{4}$ off |   | the whole amount |

* To find 20% of an amount you find _____ % of it then _____ this.

## Unit test

**1  a** Write 0.9 as a percentage. ........................   **b** Write 68% as a decimal. ........................

   **c** Write 75% as a fraction. Write your answer in its simplest form.

........................

**2  a** Write 0.72 as a percentage. ........................   **b** Write 6% as a decimal. ........................

**3** Write these numbers in order of size. Start with the smallest number.

75%      0.7      $\frac{4}{5}$

.................................................................................................

**4  a** Work out   10% of £90 ........................   **b** Work out   10% of £75 ........................

**5  a** Work out   5% of £100 ........................   **b** Work out   20% of £400 ........................

**6** Amy wants to buy a phone. The phone costs £180 plus VAT at 20%.
Work out the amount of VAT Amy pays.

£ ........................

**7** A bill was £45 plus VAT at 20%. Work out the VAT to be paid.

£ ........................

**8** Ali wants to buy a jacket. The cost of the jacket is £84. He pays a 25% deposit.
Work out 25% of £84.

£ ........................

**9** A café bill is £36.00. A tip of 10% is added.
Complete the bill to show the total cost
including the tip.

| Café bill | |
|---|---|
| Lunch and drinks | £36.00 |
| + Tip at 10% | £ ........................ |
| Total | £ ........................ |

**Example**

# 7.1

# Read and order amounts of money

By the end of this section you will know how to:

* Order and compare amounts of money
* Record amounts of money correctly

## Key points

* There are 100 pence in one pound (£1).

* Amounts of money in pounds and pence are recorded as a whole number and a decimal part with two decimal places.

* When displaying an amount of money in pounds, a calculator display of 8.4 means £8.40, 0.3 means £0.30 or 30p, and 0.67 means £0.67 or 67p.

**1** Count up the money in each purse, and record it correctly in pounds and pence.

**Hint**

Write £6.50 or £6.05, never £6.5 or £6.50p.

a

£2 + £1 + 50p + 20p + 10p + 5p

= £ ............

b

................................................................

= £ ............

c

................................................................

= £ ............

d

................................................................

= £ ............

**Practice**

**2** Write these items in order of their price. Start with the cheapest.

| | |
|---|---|
| Cheese | £1.75 |
| Apples | £1.30 |
| Lettuce | 90p |
| Eggs | £2.08 |
| Cream | 83p |

.................................... ............

.................................... ............

.................................... ............

.................................... ............

.................................... ............

**3** Work out the total amounts of money.

    **a**   3 × £7.50 = £ .............

    **b**   £2.25 × 8 = £ .............

    **c**   £3.75 × 16 = £ .............

    **d**   £20 ÷ 8 = £ .............

    **e**   £40.50 ÷ 10 = £ .............

    **f**   £750.60 ÷ 15 = £ .............

    **g**   £45.70 + £32.80 = £ .............

    **h**   £682.50 − £352.99 = £ .............

    **i**   £3.15 + 65p = £ .............

    **j**   £2.09 − 7p = £ .............

    **k**   The total of the amounts in **a** to **j**   £ .............

> **Hint**
>
> When calculating amounts of money in pounds, a calculator display of 4.5 means £4.50. 45p needs be entered as 0.45

---

Need more practice ☐     Almost there ☐     Got it! ☐

# 7.2 Calculating with money

By the end of this section you will know how to:

  ✳ Add, subtract, multiply and divide amounts of money with and without a calculator

  ✳ Work out bills, wages and budgets

  ✳ Work out simple interest and repayments, including rounding to the nearest penny

## Key points

  ✳ Managing money is an essential life skill.

  ✳ Paying bills, tax, working out simple interest and being able to budget are important.

  ✳ You will use all the skills you have learned so far in this chapter.

**Example**

**1** Match up the prices with their change from £10.

| £3.45 | £5.15 | £5.65 | £9.05 |
|-------|-------|-------|-------|
| £0.95 | £4.50 | £3.35 | £7.65 |
| £2.35 | £1.25 | £6.55 | £4.85 |
| £6.65 | £4.35 | £5.50 | £8.75 |

£3.45 + £6.55 = £10        ............ + ............ = £10

............ + ............ = £10        ............ + ............ = £10

............ + ............ = £10        ............ + ............ = £10

............ + ............ = £10        ............ + ............ = £10

## Working out the cost

> **Hint**
>
> How to add, subtract, multiply and divide decimals.

**Example**

**2** Use the prices of the items on the list to work out the cost.

    **a**   4 rolls of wallpaper   4 × £ ............ = £ ............

    **b**   1 pack of brushes and a packet of paste

         £ ............ + £0.85 = £ ............

    **c**   2 litres of paint   £ ............ × ............ = £ ............

    **d**   3 rolls of wallpaper, a litre of paint and a pack of brushes

         3 × £ ............ + £ ............ + £ ............ = £ ............

| | |
|---|---|
| Wallpaper | £10 a roll |
| Wallpaper paste | 85p a packet |
| Brushes (5) | £2.50 a pack |
| Paint | £12.50 for 1 litre |

**Practice**

**3 a** Work out the total cost of these items.

| Bread | £1.20 |
|-------|-------|
| Butter | 95p |
| Cheese | £1.80 |
| TOTAL | |

**b** Write the correct coins to pay the bill with the **exact** money.

........................................................................................................

**Extend**

**4 a** Sasha buys a sandwich and cake. She pays with two £2 coins. How much change should she get?

Take Away Snack Menu

| Sandwich | £2.50 |
|----------|-------|
| Cake | £1.25 |
| Crisps | 65p |
| Drink | 80p |

........................................................................................................

**b** Chris buys a packet of crisps and a drink. Write two ways that she could pay for this with the **exact** money.

........................................................................................................

**c** Alan wants to buy one of each item. He has £5.
Does he have enough money?
Write your calculations.

☐ Yes          ☐ No

**Example**

**5** Work out the cost of each bill. Record your calculation.

**a** 250 minutes on a phone at 11 pence per minute       250 × 0.11 = £ ...............

**b** 2745 units of electricity at 15p per unit       2745 × ............... = £ ...............

**c** Wages at £8 an hour for 22 hours    ............... × ............... = £ ...............

**d** Five friends pay £9 for a pizza. They share the cost equally. How much does each person pay?

£9 ÷ ............... = 1.8 = £1. ...............

**Practice**

**6** Work out the total amounts. Record your calculation.

**Hint**
1 year = 12 months = 52 weeks;
1 month is about 4 weeks.

**a** Rent at £750 per month for a year    ....................................................

**b** Saving £15 per week for a year    ....................................................

**c** A newspaper costs 60p on weekdays, £1 on Saturdays and £1.20 on Sundays.
Work out the cost of having a newspaper every day for 2 weeks.

£ ....................................................

44

**d** Lois buys 5 magazines @ £3.75 each.
How much change does she get from £20?

£ .............................

**e** Nick bought four large cakes. He paid £10.
How much was each cake?

£ .............................

**7** Molly earns £700 a month. She saves 20%.
How much does she spend?

.............................

> **Hint**
> The interest rate is a percentage charge made on money loaned or paid on money saved. It is usually given as a rate per year.

### Simple interest

**8** How much interest will these savers have at the end of the year?

**a** Mari: £400 at 5%      $400 \times 5 \div 100 = £$ ............

**b** Tomas: £450 at 4%     $450 \times$ ............ $\div$ ............ $= £$ ............

**c** Zoe: £360 at 7%      ............ $\times$ ............ $\div$ ............ $= £$ ............

**d** Andi: £320 at 8%     ............................ $= £$ ............

> **Hint**
> To find a percentage on a calculator, multiply the amount by the percentage then divide by 100.

**9** How much extra per year will these borrowers have to pay on their loan?

**a** Lisa: £8000 car, paying interest at 12%      ..............................................

**b** Sol: £450 computer, paying interest at 11%      ..............................................

**c** Liz: £180 000 house, paying interest at 6%      ..............................................

**d** Tony: £1500 holiday, paying interest at 14%      ..............................................

### Repayments (interest-free loans)

**10** Work out how much needs to be paid each month, after the deposit is paid.

**a** £400 over 6 months, £40 deposit

£400 − £40 = £360      £360 ÷ 6 = £ ........ per month

**b** £1500 over 1 year, deposit of 20%

20% of £1500 = £ ........      £1500 − £ ........ = £ ........      £ ........ ÷ 12 = £ ........ per month

**c** £2500 over 8 months, £500 deposit

............ − ............ = £ ........      ............ ÷ ............ = £ ........ per month

**Practice**

**11** Work out how much must be paid each month, after the deposit is paid. Show your calculations.

a £750 over 10 months, £50 deposit

......................................................................................................................

b £3600 over a year, 5% deposit

......................................................................................................................

**Extend**

**12** A car costs £5000. Ian pays a deposit of £500. He will pay the rest monthly over a year. How much will he pay each month?

£ .......................................

**Rounding money**

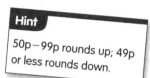

Hint
50p – 99p rounds up; 49p or less rounds down.

**Example**

**13** Write all the numbers on the calculator display, then round to the nearest penny.

a £240 ÷ 7 = 34.28571429 = £34.29

Hint
How to round decimals to the nearest whole one and to one decimal place.

b £550 ÷ 9 = 61.111111111 = £ ............ . ......

c £125 ÷ 13 = ....... . .................... = £ ......... . ......    d £1100 ÷ 15 = ....... . .................... = £ ......... . ......

e £12 ÷ 7 = ............................... = £ ........    f £47 ÷ 8 = ............................... = £ ........

**Practice**

**14** Round each amount to the nearest pound.

a £34.75   £ ...............    b £54.19   £ ...............    c £76.81   £ ...............

d £83.45   £ ...............    e £184.56   £ ...............    f £365.99   £ ...............

**Practice**

**15** Round each amount to the nearest 10 pence.

a £27.34   £ ...............    b £12.78   £ ...............    c £72.52   £ ...............

d £835.48   £ ...............    e £354.09   £ ...............    f £65.99   £ ...............

## Earning money and budgeting

Example

**16** How much does each person earn?

   **a** Heather works for 16 hours at £8.25 an hour.     16 × £8.25 = £...........

   **b** Peter works for 33 hours at £12.75 an hour.   ........... × £......... = £...........

   **c** Sunil earns £720 for 80 hours' work. How much per hour? £......... ÷ ......... = £......... per hour

   **d** Kris earns £320 for 14 hours' work. How much per hour (round to nearest penny)?

     £......... ÷ ...... = £......... . 85714286 = £......... . ...... per hour

Practice

**17** Work out the amounts earned.

   **a** 32 hours at £14 per hour                  **b** £2100 for 4 weeks

                                 £...........                        £........... per week

   **c** £22 260 per year                    **d** 56 hours at £19.25 per hour

                  £........... per month                      £...........

   **e** £560 for 25 hours' work        **f** £125 for 11 hours

              £........... per hour                 £........... per hour
                                                              (to nearest 1p)

Extend

**18 a** Dave works 8 hours per day, 5 days per week at an hourly rate of £15. How much does he earn in a week?

                                                 £........................

   **b** Sarah works 6 hours a day, 6 days a week. She earns £441 in a week.
       What is her hourly rate?

                                               £........................

   **c** Lily is 16 years old. She works on weekends and earns £80 a month. Suggest a monthly budget for Lily.

     Clothes  £.........       Phone  £.........       Entertainment  £.........       Savings  £.........

## Calculating bills

**Example**

**19 a** Here is part of Richard's electricity bill. Work out the total cost of the units used.

> **Electricity Bill**                                December 2012
>
> R Johns
> 2 Woodlands Drive
> Cheltenham
>
> Reading 1st December            3129 units
> Reading 1st September           2572 units
>
> Number of units used    ............ units    3129 – 2572 = ............ units
>
> Cost: £0.18 per unit    18 × ............ = ............ pence = £ ....... . .......

**b** Jimmy has a mobile phone.

He has to pay 11p for every minute of calls and pay 8p for every text he sends.
Last month Jimmy:

 * made a total of 180 minutes of calls
 * sent 250 texts.

Work out how much Jimmy had to pay last month.

Calls = £0.11 × ................................................    Texts = £ ................................................

Total = £ ................................................

**Practice**

**20** Work out the total cost of a trip to the cinema.

```
3 adult cinema tickets at £8.25   = ............
2 children's tickets at £4.75     = ............
1 large popcorn at £4.99          = ............

Total                             = ............
```

£ ............................

**Extend**

**21** This is Renée's phone bill. Work out the total cost for November.

> **Phone Bill**                    November 2012
>
> R Holland
> 22 Regent Ave
> Liverpool
>
> Rental for November        £14.25
> Minutes used in November   320
> Cost:                      £0.12 per minute

£ ............................

## Don't forget!

\* Circle the amounts of money that are correctly recorded.

£3.40p          £3.04          £5.4          £0.99p          £0.99

\* Match the calculations to the questions.

5 rolls of wrapping paper at £2.50 each

Sally receives £32.50 for 5 hours' work. What is her hourly rate?

What is the cost of 250 minutes on a phone at 15p per minute?

20% VAT on TV costing £250

**32.50 ÷ 5**

**250 × 0.15**

**5 × 2.50**

**250 ÷ 20**

**5 ÷ 32.50**

**250 ÷ 10 × 2**

## Unit test

**1** Tahreem buys 4 books at £4.50 each. She pays with a £20 note.
How much change does she get?

£ ............................

**2** One pencil costs £0.55. Ollie buys 10 of these pencils.
Work out the total cost.

£ ............................

**3** Work out   £10 − £4.15

£ ............................

**4** Elli spent £2.95. She paid with a £10 note. How much change did she get?

£ ............................

**5** Here is a table that can be used to find
the cost of rolls of sticky tape.

**a** Work out the cost of 16 rolls.

£ ............................

**b** Work out the cost of 24 rolls.

£ ............................

| Number of rolls | Cost |
|---|---|
| 1 | 45p |
| 2 | 90p |
| 3 | £1.35 |
| 4 | £1.80 |
| 5 | £2.25 |
| 6 | £2.70 |
| 7 | £3.15 |
| 8 | £3.60 |
| 9 | £4.05 |
| 10 | £4.50 |

**6** Ewan bought a car for £4000. He paid a deposit of 20%.
How much deposit did he pay?

£ ...........................

**7** Ceris bought some items from a shop. She bought:

| | |
|---|---|
| 2 notebooks at | £3.25 each |
| 5 pencils at | 35p each |
| 1 sharpener at | £1.05 each |

How much did Ceris spend?

£ ...........................

**8** Here is Stuart's phone bill.

**Phone Bill**                    January 2012

S Bradley
2 King's Meadow
Bristol

| | |
|---|---|
| Rental for January | £14.75 |
| Minutes used in January | 280 |
| Cost: | £0.15 per minute |

Work out the total cost of the units used.

Work out the total cost of Stuart's phone bill for January.

£ ...........................

**9** Work out the cost of 12 packs of biscuits at 85 pence each.

£ ...........................

# Read, record and measure time

**8.1**

By the end of this section you will know how to:

* Read time on analogue and digital clocks
* Convert between 12-hour time and 24-hour time
* Use the correct notation for 24-hour times

## Key points

* Before 12 o'clock midday is shown as **am**.

* After midday until midnight is shown as **pm**.

* Digital time is recorded using four digits such as 01:45 and 23 54.

* There are 24 hours in a whole day, made up of two sets of 12 hours.

*Example*

**1** Write these times in words, 12-hour time and 24-hour time.

**a** 7.30 am

half past ............... / 7.30 ...... / 07: ......

**b** 6.15 pm

> **Hint**
> Add 12 to get the 24-hour time.

............... past ......... / 6. ......pm / 18: ......

**c** 3.45 am

quarter ...... ......... / ............... / .........

**d** 8.50 pm

> **Hint**
> Add 12 to get the 24-hour time.

ten to ......... / ............... / 20: ......

*Practice*

**2** Show these times on the analogue clocks. Then write the 24-hour time in the space below.

**a** twenty past eight in the morning

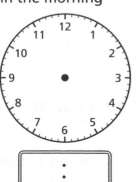

**b** 8.45 pm

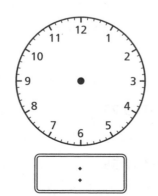

**c** 2.55 am

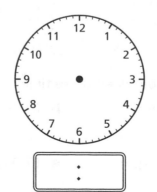

**d** twenty to ten at night

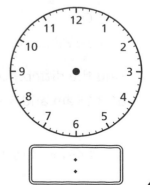

Extend

**3 a** Change these times to 24-hour times.

4.30 pm ........:........        5.20 am ........:........        11.35 pm ........:........        9.50 am ........:........

**b** Change these 24-hour times into 12-hour times using am or pm.

09:30 ................        22:25 ................        03:05 ................        16:44 ................

**c** Write these times in 12-hour am/pm and in 24-hour time.

twenty-five past eleven in the morning                five to six in the evening

.................     .................                .................     .................

---

Need more practice ☐        Almost there ☐        Got it! ☐

# Use units of time

## 8.2

By the end of this section you will know how to:

* Read and interpret timetables
* Work out durations of time

**Key points**

* Most timetables use 24-hour digital times, so use 16:30 to show 4.30 pm.

> **Hint**
> 60 seconds = 1 minute;
> 60 minutes = 1 hour;
> 24 hours = 1 day.

**Example**

**1** Find the difference between the times shown on the two clocks.

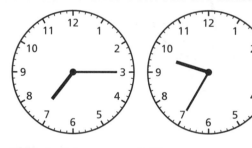

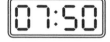

**a** 7.15 + **2 hours** = 9.15
9.15 + **20 min** = 9.35

Time difference = ........ hours ........ minutes

**b** 07:50 + 10 min = 08:00
08:00 + 20 min = 08:20

Time difference = ........ minutes

> **Hint**
> When the numbers of minutes are close, sometimes it is more efficient to add on whole hours then count back.

**c** 4.35 + ........ min = 5.00
5.00 + 1 ........ = 6.00
6.00 + ........ ........ = 6.05

Time difference = ........ hour ........ minutes

**d** 19:25 + ........ hours = 23:25
23:25 − ........ min = 23:20

Time difference = ........ hours ........ minutes

**Practice**

**2** Find the differences between these times.

**a** 3.15 am and 5.20 am        **b** 07:50 and 09:25        **c** 18:55 and 20:40

.................................        .................................        .................................

**d** 14.45 pm and 17.35 pm        **e** 07:05 and 12:55        **f** 22.30 pm and 1.15 am

.................................        .................................        .................................

**52**

**Practice**

**3** Here is part of the train timetable from Eastam to Southwood.

| Eastam to Southwood | | | | | | | |
|---|---|---|---|---|---|---|---|
| Eastam | 06:11 | 07:05 | 08:22 | 09:25 | 10:09 | 10:56 | 11:43 |
| Northlee | 06:26 | 07:19 | 08:36 | 09:42 | 10:33 | 11:10 | 11:58 |
| Westfield | 06:54 | 07:51 | 09:03 | 10:17 | 11:01 | 11:39 | 12:27 |
| Southwood | 07:09 | 08:02 | 09:19 | 10:24 | 11:18 | 11:55 | 12:41 |

**a** Which train should you catch from Eastam to arrive in Southwood for 10.30 am? ...............

**b** How long does the 08:22 train take to get from Eastam to Southwood? ............... minutes

**c** Which train should you catch from Eastam to arrive in Westfield by 8 am? ...............

**d** How long does the 10:09 train take to get from Northlee to Westfield? ............... minutes

**e** Which train journey from Eastam to Southwood is faster – the 06:11 or the 10:56?
Show your working.

06:11 ............... minutes        10:56 ............... minutes        Faster ...............

**f** Ellen arrives at Westfield station at twenty-five past eight in the morning.

How long will she have to wait for the next train to Southwood? ............... minutes

**Extend**

**4** Here is a gym timetable.

**a** Find out how long each class lasts. The next class starts as the previous one finishes.

| Class | Start time |
|---|---|
| Step | 09:00 |
| Circuits | 10:10 |
| Zumba | 10:55 |
| Kettle Bells | 12:10 |
| Pilates | 12:50 |

Length of class: ...............
Length of class: ...............
Length of class: ...............
Length of class: ...............

**b** Lynsey wants to go to the Step and Zumba classes.
How long will she exercise in total? ............... minutes

**c** It takes Mike 25 minutes to get to the gym and be ready to start. What is the latest time he can set off to be in time for Kettle Bells?

........... : ...........

**d** Paulo sets off from home at 09:35 to attend the Circuits class. He spends 10 minutes in the changing room before the class. How long is his journey to the gym?

............... minutes

**5** These are the times in hours, minutes and seconds for three marathon runners. Who won?

**Jack**            **Ben**            **Jason**

| 02:46:17 |        | 02:45:59 |        | 02:46:09 |

...............

# 8.3 Convert between units of time

By the end of this section you will know how to:

* convert between different units of time

## Key points

* 1 day is 24 hours; 1 week is 7 days; 1 year is 12 months.
* 1 hour is 60 minutes; 1 minute is 60 seconds.
* 1 year is 365 days, 52 weeks or 12 months.

**Practice**

**1** Use the numbers in the box to complete the statements about time.

| 1 | 2 | 12 | 30 | 52 | 60 | 240 | 366 |

a ........ months = 1 year    b ........ hour = ........ minutes    c ........ seconds = 4 minutes

d ........ minutes = half an hour    e ........ weeks = 1 year    f ........ days in a leap year

**Example**

**2** Convert these units of time.

a 5 hours into minutes        5 × 60 = 300 minutes

b 36 months into years        36 ÷ 12 = 3 years

c 60 minutes into seconds     60 × ........ = ........ seconds

d 416 weeks into years        ........ ÷ ........ = ........ years

e 315 days into weeks         ........ ÷ ........ = ........ weeks

f 72 hours into days          ........ ÷ ........ = ........ days

g 24 hours into **seconds**   24 × ........ × ........ = ........ seconds

**Practice**

**3** Use multiplication and division to convert these times.

a 4 days = ........ hours    b 56 days = ........ weeks    c 10 minutes = ........ seconds

d ........ months = 6 years    e 420 minutes = ........ hours    f ........ years = 48 months

**Extend**

**4** Work out the answers.

a Eryk is at college 5 days a week for 32 weeks. How many days is that?

........................ days

b The TV programme lasts $2\frac{1}{4}$ hours.
How many minutes are there in $2\frac{1}{4}$ hours?    ........................ minutes

c Susie cycles at a speed of 12 miles per hour. She cycles for 3 hours.
How many miles does she cycle?    ........................ miles

d Joe travelled 100 miles in 2 hours. How many miles per hour is that?    ........................ miles per hour

# Use calendars

**8.4**

By the end of this section you will know how to:

* Read, use and complete calendars
* Work out dates that are not shown

**Key points**

* A calendar usually covers a whole year and each month is shown separately.
* There are 30 days in April, June, September and November.
* There are 28 days in February, except in a leap year, when there are 29.
* A **leap year** happens every four years when the year is a multiple of 4.

> **Hint**
>
> A year that is a multiple of 100 is **not** a leap year unless it is a multiple of 1000.

**Practice**

**1** Use the rhyme to fill in the number of days for each month.

| | | | |
|---|---|---|---|
| January ......... | February ......... | March ......... | April ......... |
| May ......... | June ......... | July ......... | August ......... |
| September ......... | October ......... | November ......... | December ......... |

> **Hint**
>
> 30 days has September, April, June and November, all the rest have 31, except February, which has 28 days clear and 29 each leap year.

**Example**

**2 a** Here is part of a calendar. Fill in the missing calendar dates.

| June 2013 | | | | | | |
|---|---|---|---|---|---|---|
| **Sun** | **Mon** | **Tues** | **Wed** | **Thurs** | **Fri** | **Sat** |
| | | | | | | |
| | | 4 | 5 | | | 8 |
| | 10 | 11 | | | 14 | 15 |
| 16 | 17 | | 19 | | | |
| | | 25 | | 27 | | |
| | | | | | | |

> **Hint**
>
> The shaded dates show the last few days of the month before and the next few days after the month displayed.

**b** What day of the week is 20 June 2013? ..........................

**c** What is the date of the next Tuesday after 15 June 2013? ..........................

**d** Juliana wants to have her birthday party on the Friday nearest to her birthday. Her birthday is on 12 June 2013. On which date should she have her party? ..........................

**e** What date is 2 weeks before 8 June 2013?

   I week before is ............ June, so 2 weeks before is ............ May

**f** What date is 4 weeks after 25 June 2013?   $25 - 2 =$ ......., so ..........................

**g** What day of the week is 27 May 2013?   27 May is ..........................

> **Hint**
>
> Use 4 weeks = 28 days.
> Example: To work out 4 weeks after 21 January: January has 31 (or 28 + 3) days: 21 − 3 = 18. So 4 weeks after 21 January is 18 February

## Don't forget!

\* Match the 12-hour times to the 24-hour times.

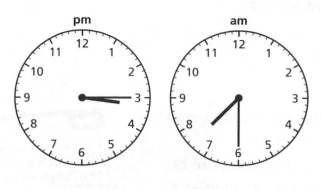

ten past ten
in the
evening

ten to nine
in the
morning

| 22:10 | 08:50 | 15:15 | 07:30 |

\* Complete the time conversi\ons.

4 hours = .......... minutes          36 months = .......... years          .......... weeks = 49 days

.......... minutes = 300 seconds          .......... hours = 2 days          3 hours = .......... seconds

\* When 31 March is on a Tuesday, 3 April will be on a ........................

When 1 May is a Wednesday, 29 April is on a ........................

## Unit test

1   Here is a TV timetable.

| Programme | Start time |
|-----------|------------|
| News      | 18:15      |
| Sport     | 18:50      |
| Cartoon   | 20:25      |
| Film      | 21:10      |
| Late news | 23:55      |

a  How long is the film?     .......... hours .......... minutes

b  How long is the cartoon?          .......... minutes

c  Jamie watches the film and the cartoon.
   What is his total viewing time?

.......... hours .......... minutes

2   Here is a clock face and a digital display.
    Draw hands on the clock to show a time of
    **twenty-five to eight in the evening.**
    Write the numbers on the digital display to
    show the same time.

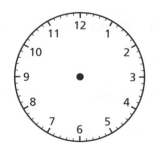

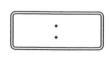

**3** Write down in words the time shown on the clocks.

**a**

**b**

**c**

..................................    ..................................    ..................................

**4** Here is part of the bus timetable from Warden Hill to Bishop's Cleeve.

| Warden Hill to Bishop's Cleeve | | | | | | | |
|---|---|---|---|---|---|---|---|
| Warden Hill | 07:15 | 07:55 | 08:35 | 07:15 | 09:55 | 10:35 | 11:15 |
| Cheltenham | 07:42 | 08:22 | 09:02 | 09:42 | 10:22 | 11:02 | 11:42 |
| Bishop's Cleeve | 08:01 | 08:41 | 09:21 | 10:01 | 10:41 | 11:21 | 12:01 |

**a** Which bus should you catch from Warden Hill to arrive in Cheltenham for 10.30 am?

..................................

**b** How long does the 07:55 bus take to get from Warden Hill to Bishop's Cleeve? ............ minutes

**c** Which part of the journey is quicker: Warden Hill to Cheltenham or Cheltenham to Bishop's Cleeve? Show your working.

..................................

**5** Here is part of a calendar for October 2012.

| October 2012 | | | | | | |
|---|---|---|---|---|---|---|
| Sun | Mon | Tues | Wed | Thurs | Fri | Sat |
|  | 1 | 2 | 3 | 4 | 5 | 6 |
| 7 | 8 | 9 | 10 | 11 | 12 | 13 |
| 14 | 15 | 16 | 17 | 18 | 19 | 20 |
|  |  |  |  |  |  |  |
|  |  |  |  |  |  |  |

**a** What day of the week is 17 October? ..................................

**b** What day of the week is 21 October? ..................................

**c** What is the date two weeks after 15 October? ..................................

**d** What is the date two weeks before 9 October? ..................................

**e** What is the date four weeks after 20 October? ..................................

# 9.1 Read, write, order and compare integers

By the end of this section you will know how to:

* Read and write integers of any size
* Order and compare positive and negative integers of any size

## Key points

* Number lines can be used to help you order and compare positive and negative integers.

* On a horizontal number line, the further a number is to the left the smaller it is.

> **Hint**
> An **integer** is a positive or negative whole number, including zero. The word **negative** is used to identify numbers less than zero.

**Example**

**1 a** Write the number **three thousand, four hundred and twelve** in figures. 341......

**b** Write the number **15 706** in words. fifteen thousand, seven ..................... and ..............

**c** What is the value of the **2** in the number 23 705? ......................................................

**2** Write these numbers in order of size. Start with the smallest number.

> **Hint**
> You can use a number line to help you answer this type of question.

**a** −3, 4, −6, 3, 7      −6, −3, 3, .................................................

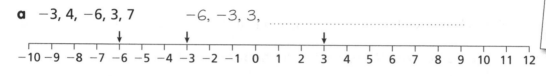

**b** 9, −5, −8, 11, 0      −8, .................................................

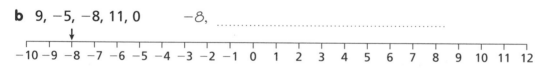

**c** 2, −6, −10, 5, −8      .................................................

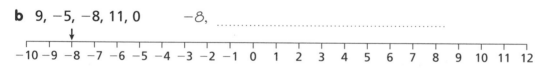

**Practice**

**3** Write these numbers in order of size.

**a** −9, 20, 17, −17, −20

smallest ................................................................... largest

**b** 12, −16, 0, 8, −10

largest ................................................................... smallest

**c** −11, 9, −15, −22, 10

smallest ................................................................... largest

# 9.2 Add and subtract integers

By the end of this section you will know how to:

* Add positive and negative integers of any size without a calculator
* Subtract positive and negative integers of any size without a calculator

## Key points

* Adding a negative number is the same as subtracting a positive number.
* Subtracting a negative number is the same as adding a positive number.
* For addition and subtraction of larger numbers you must line up the digits in the correct columns.

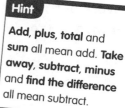

**Hint**

Add, **plus, total** and **sum** all mean add. **Take away, subtract, minus** and **find the difference** all mean subtract.

**Example**

**1** Work out

**a** $-3 + -5$

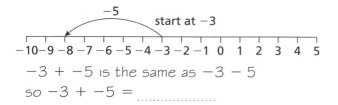

$-3 + -5$ is the same as $-3 - 5$
so $-3 + -5 =$ ..................

**b** $-7 - -2$

start at $-7$

$-10\,-9\,-8\,-7\,-6\,-5\,-4\,-3\,-2\,-1\ 0\ 1\ 2\ 3\ 4\ 5$

$-7 - -2$ is the same as $-7 + 2$
so $-7 - -2 =$ ..................

**c** $-1 + -8$

$-10\,-9\,-8\,-7\,-6\,-5\,-4\,-3\,-2\,-1\ 0\ 1\ 2\ 3\ 4\ 5$

$-1 + -8$ is the same as $-1$ ..................
so $-1 + -8 =$ ..................

**d** $-4 - -6$

$-10\,-9\,-8\,-7\,-6\,-5\,-4\,-3\,-2\,-1\ 0\ 1\ 2\ 3\ 4\ 5$

$-4 - -6$ is the same as ..................
so $-4 - -6 =$ ..................

**Practice**

**2** Work out

**a** $3 + -8$

..........................

**b** $6 - -4$

..........................

**c** $-9 + -2$

..........................

**d** $-5 - -1$

..........................

**e** $7 - 10$

..........................

**f** $-3 + -4$

..........................

**Extend**

**3** The temperature in Moscow one evening is $-4$°C.

At night the temperature falls by 7°C.

What is the night temperature in Moscow?

..........................°C

**59**

**Example**

**4** Work out

**a** 396 + 547

```
    3 9 6
  + 5 4 7
  ─────────
      4 3
    ........
     | |
```

**b** 1053 + 768

```
  1 0 5 3
  +   7 6 8
  ─────────
          |
    ........
     |
```

**c** 21 408 + 5706 + 431

```
  2 1 4 0 8
  .................
  + .................
  ─────────────
  .................
```

**5** Work out

**a** 423 − 159

```
    4 2 ¹3
  − 1 5 9
  ─────────
        4
    ........
```

**b** 2108 − 329

```
    2 1 0 ¹8
  −     3 2 9
  ─────────────
            9
    ............
```

**c** 11 502 + 3650 − 10 463

```
  1 1 5 0 2
  + .................
  ─────────────
  .................
```

```
  .................
  − 1 0 4 6 3
  ─────────────
  .................
```

**Hint**

First do the addition then the subtraction.

**Practice**

**6** Work out

**a** 5476 + 21 853

**b** 13 558 + 7406 + 22 253

**c** 4321 − 872

**d** 6572 − 3897

**e** 74 113 + 4327 − 32 548

**f** 26 050 + 6994 − 17 058

Need more practice ☐     Almost there ☐     Got it! ☐

# Multiply and divide integers

## 9.3

By the end of this section you will know how to:

✳ Multiply positive integers of any size without a calculator

✳ Divide positive integers of any size without a calculator

### Key points

✳ You can use a grid to help you multiply large numbers together.

✳ You can use short division (or long division) to divide into large numbers.

✳ You need to know your tables facts to multiply and divide integers.

**Hint**

**Times** means multiply. A **product** is the result of multiplication. **Share** means divide.

60

**1** Work out

**a** 28 × 54

| ×  | 50   | 4  |
|----|------|----|
| 20 | 1000 | ......... |
| 8  | 400  | 32 |

28 × 54 = 1000
+   400
+  ........
+    32
    1512

**b** 346 × 47

**c** 261 × 35

**2** Work out

**a** 224 ÷ 7

$$\begin{array}{r} 3........ \\ 7\overline{)2\phantom{0}2\phantom{0}^14} \end{array}$$

**b** 3858 ÷ 6

**c** 4600 ÷ 8

**3** Work out

**a** 453 × 72

**b** 807 × 39

**c** 317 × 85

**d** 4077 ÷ 9

**e** 2702 ÷ 7

**f** 5232 ÷ 6

Need more practice ▢    Almost there ▢    Got it! ▢

# 9.4 Multiply and divide using negative integers

By the end of this section you will know how to:

* ✱ Multiply using negative integers without a calculator
* ✱ Divide using negative integers without a calculator

**Key points**

✱ When multiplying and dividing with negative integers:

• if the signs are the same the result is positive

• if the signs are different the result is negative.

**Example**

1 Work out

a $13 \times -3 = +13 \times -3$     signs are different     answer = $-$ ....9....

b $-7 \times -4$     signs are the same     answer = ................

c $-5 \times 11 =$ ........................     signs are ......................     answer = ................

2 Work out

a $24 \div -3 = +24 \div -3$     signs are different     answer = ................

b $-12 \div -4$     signs are the same     answer = ................

c $\dfrac{-20}{5} =$ ........................     signs are ......................     answer = ................

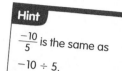

> **Hint**
>
> $\dfrac{-10}{5}$ is the same as $-10 \div 5$.

**Practice**

3 Work out

a $-6 \times -3$

b $\dfrac{30}{-10}$

c $8 \times -7$

..............................     ..............................     ..............................

d $-42 \div -6$

e $-9 \times 4$

f $\dfrac{-27}{3}$

..............................     ..............................     ..............................

Need more practice ☐     Almost there ☐     Got it! ☐

# 9.5 Read, write and use squares, cubes and square roots

By the end of this section you will know how to:

✳ Square and cube numbers

✳ Find the square root of a number

**Key points**

✳ A **square number** is the result of multiplying a number by itself.

✳ A **cube number** is the result of multipling a number by itself and then multiplying the answer by the original number.

✳ The **square root** of a number is a value that, when multiplied by itself, gives the number.

✳ You can use the $\boxed{\sqrt{\phantom{x}}}$ button on your calculator to work out the square root of a number.

**Example**

1 Write down the squares of the following numbers.

a 3     3 squared $= 3 \times 3 =$ ..........

b 21     21 squared $= 21 \times$ ........ $=$ ..........

c 95     95 squared $=$ ........................ $=$ ................

> **Hint**
>
> '5 squared' means the same as 'the square of 5'.

**2** Write down the cubes of the following numbers.

**a** 5        5 cubed = 5 × 5 × 5 = ..........

**b** 8        8 cubed = 8 × ...... × ...... = ..........

**c** 11       11 cubed = ...................... = ................

**3** Write down the square roots of the following numbers.

**a** 16       $\sqrt{16}$ is **4** because 4 × 4 = ..........

**b** 25       $\sqrt{25}$ is ...... because ...... × ...... = 25

**c** 36       $\sqrt{36}$ is ...... because ...... × ...... = ..........

**4** Which of the numbers in the box are:

| 4 | 49 | 27 | 64 | 81 | 100 | 36 |
|---|----|----|----|----|-----|----|

**a** square numbers                    **b** cube numbers?

................................................              ................................................

**5** Work out

**a** $\sqrt{121}$                **b** $\sqrt{169}$                **c** $\sqrt{225}$

................................................              ................................................              ................................................

**Need more practice** ☐    **Almost there** ☐    **Got it!** ☐

# Use index notation

## 9.6

By the end of this section you will know how to:

✳ Use index notation for small positive integer powers

### Key points

✳ A number written in the form $a^n$ is in index form, where $n$ is called the **index** or **power**.

✳ The index tells you how many times the number is multiplied by itself.

✳ If the power is 2 you can use the $\boxed{x^2}$ key on your calculator.

✳ If the power is 3 you can use the $\boxed{x^3}$ key on your calculator.

✳ For other powers use the $\boxed{x^n}$ key.

**1** Work out

**a** $3^4$                    **b** $5^3$                    **c** $2^5$

= 3 × 3 × 3 × 3            = 5 × 5 × ......            = 2 × ...............................

= ..........                = ................            = ..........

**Practice**

**2** Work out

a  $4^4$

b  $2^4 \times 6^2$

c  $6^3 \times 8^2$

**Hint**

Example: You can work out $5^4$ on your calculator by pressing

$\boxed{5}\ \boxed{x^n}\ \boxed{4}\ \boxed{=}$

..........................    ..........................    ..........................

**Extend**

**3** Work out  $5^2 \times \sqrt{100}$

..........................

## Don't forget!

✳ Draw a line to match each term with its definition.

| **integer** | **prime number** | **multiple** | **factor** |
|---|---|---|---|
| number divisible only by itself and 1 | integer that divides exactly into a number | whole number | result of multiplying by an integer |

✳ When comparing positive and negative numbers, the further a number is to the right the

.......................... it is.

✳ Complete the following:

$12\,758 + 4567 - 11\,245 =$ .................. $- 11\,245 =$ ..............

$347 \times 35 =$ ..................          $9728 \div 8 =$ ..............

✳ Match each question in bold with the correct answer below.

**LCM of 12 and 8**          **$2^3$**          **HCF of 12 and 8**          **$\sqrt{36}$**

8          24          6          4

✳ Complete the following:

$16 = 2 \cdots$        $-8 = 4 \times$ ..........        $-11 = -7 +$ ..........        $4 = \dfrac{-12}{......}$

## Unit test

**1 a** Write the number **thirteen thousand, six hundred and fourteen** in figures.

..........................

**b** Write the number **20 311** in words.

..........................

**c** Write down the value of the **6** in the number 26 783.

..........................

**2** Write these numbers in order of size. Start with the smallest number.

2    −3    1    −5    0

..........................

**3 a** Work out   $-5 \times 7$

..........................

**b** Work out   $-7 + 5$

..........................

**c** Work out   $-8 \times -2$

..........................

**d** Work out   $-6 - 3$

..........................

**e** Work out   $\dfrac{28}{-4}$

..........................

**f** Work out   $-55 \div 11$

..........................

**4 a** Work out   $396 \times 43$

........................

**b** Work out   $468 \times 72$

........................

**c** Work out   $3616 \div 8$

........................

**d** Work out   $3303 \div 9$

........................

**5 a** Work out   $21\,735 + 5765 - 3527$

........................

**b** Work out   $1732 - 596$

........................

**6 a** Find the value of   $3^4 \times 3^3$

........................

**b** Find the value of   $\sqrt{6^2 + 8^2}$

........................

# Function machines

**10.1**

By the end of this section you will know how to:

* Work out the output from a function machine when given the input

* Work out the input from a function machine when given the output

* Use inverse operations to form function machines

## Key points

* When working out an output you work from left to right.

* When working out an input you work from right to left and use inverse operations.

**Example**

**1 a** Work out the output from this function machine.

Input ___→ [ +5 ] →___ Output
4                          ?

Output = 4 + 5 = 9

> **Hint**
> A function is a rule that changes one number into another.
> The function +5 adds 5 to a number.

> **Hint**
> Diagrams of this sort are often called flow diagrams.

**b** Here is another function machine.

6 ——→ [ ×4 ] ——→ ?

Work out the output when the input is 6.

Output = 6 ......... = .........

**2** This function machine has two operations.

5 ——→ [ ×2 ] ——→ [ +3 ] ——→ ?

Work out the output when the input is 5.

> **Hint**
> First work out 5 × 2, then add 3.

Output = (5 × 2) + 3 = ......... + 3 = .........

**Practice**

Work out the output from these function machines.

**3 a**   3 ——→ [ +6 ] ——→

Output = ..............................

**b**   20 ——→ [ ÷5 ] ——→

Output = ..............................

**c**   16 ——→ [ −9 ] ——→

Output = ..............................

**d**   11 ——→ [ ×4 ] ——→

Output = ..............................

**e**   −3 ——→ [ ×10 ] ——→

Output = ..............................

**f**   −2 ——→ [ −12 ] ——→

Output = ..............................

67

**4 a** 6 ⟶ +2 ⟶ ×5 ⟶ Output = .............................

**b** 3 ⟶ ×7 ⟶ −2 ⟶ Output = .............................

**c** 15 ⟶ ÷3 ⟶ +1 ⟶ Output = .............................

**d** 29 ⟶ −1 ⟶ ÷2 ⟶ Output = .............................

**5 a** 8 ⟶ ×2 ⟶ +1 ⟶ Output = .............................

**b** 7 ⟶ −4 ⟶ ×8 ⟶ Output = .............................

**c** 17 ⟶ +1 ⟶ ÷3 ⟶ Output = .............................

**d** 36 ⟶ ÷2 ⟶ −1 ⟶ Output = .............................

**6 a** −4 ⟶ +6 ⟶ ×9 ⟶ Output = .............................

**b** −10 ⟶ ÷2 ⟶ −3 ⟶ Output = .............................

**7 a** Work out the input from this function machine.

? ⟶ ×3 ⟶ 36

⟵ ÷3 ⟵ 36

**Hint**

You will need to use the inverse operation. The inverse function is ÷3 because it reverses the effect of the function ×3.

**Hint**

Note that the direction of the arrows is now from right to left

Input = 36 ÷ 3 = ...........

**b** Work out the input from this function machine.

? ⟶ +2 ⟶ 68

⟵ −2 ⟵ 68

**Hint**

Remember + and − are inverse operations and × and ÷ are inverse operations.

Input = 68 − 2 = ...........

**Example**

**Example**

**8 a** This function machine has two operations. Work out the input when the output is 23.

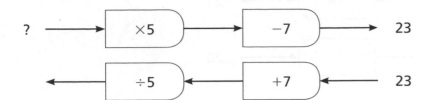

**Hint**

Draw the flow diagram of the inverse function. Arrows from right to left.

Input = (23 + 7) ÷ 5 = 30 ÷ 5 = .........

**Hint**

First add 7. Then divide by 5.

**b** Work out the input for this function when the output is 15.

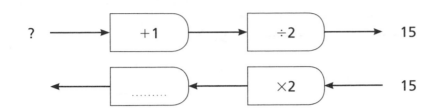

**Hint**

What is the inverse of +11?

Input = (15 × 2) ......... = 30 ......... = .........

**Practice**

Work out the input from these function machines.

**9 a**   20

Input = ...............................................

**b**   26

Input = ...............................................

**c**   48

Input = ...............................................

**d**   100

Input = ...............................................

**10 a** 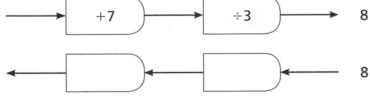  8

Input = ...............................................

**b** 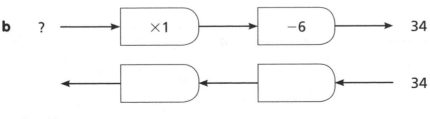  34

Input = ...............................................

**11 a**

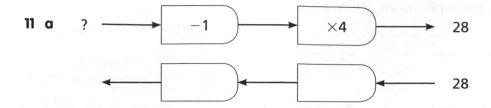

Input = ................................................................

**b**

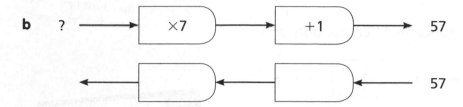

Input = ................................................................

**12 a**

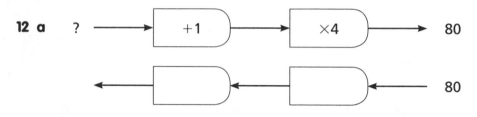

Input = ................................................................

**b**

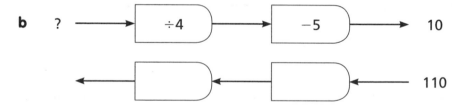

Input = ................................................................

**13 a**

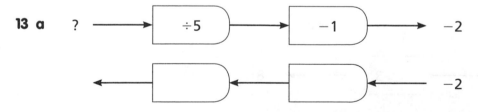

Input = ................................................................

**b**

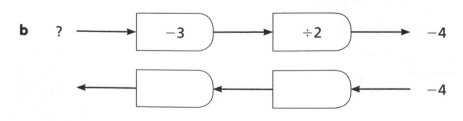

Input = ................................................................

## Don't forget!

✳ To work out an ................ you work from left to right.
✳ To work out an input you work from ............... to ............... and use ............... operations.

## Unit test

**1 a** −1 ⟶ +8 ⟶

Output = ..................................

**b** 5 ⟶ −8 ⟶

Output = ..................................

**c** 14 ⟶ ×3 ⟶

Output = ..................................

**d** 28 ⟶ ÷7 ⟶

Output = ..................................

**2** Work out the output from these function machines.

**a** 10 ⟶ −3 ⟶ ×6 ⟶      Output = ..................................

**b** 12 ⟶ ÷4 ⟶ +11 ⟶      Output = ..................................

**c** 39 ⟶ +6 ⟶ ÷9 ⟶      Output = ..................................

**d** 8 ⟶ ×6 ⟶ −5 ⟶      Output = ..................................

**3** Work out the input from these function machines.

**a** ? ⟶ ×2 ⟶ −7 ⟶ 13

⟵ ÷2 ⟵ +7 ⟵

Input = ..................................

**b** ? ⟶ +9 ⟶ ×4 ⟶ 36

⟵ −9 ⟵ ÷4 ⟵ 36

Input = ..................................

## 11.1 Multiply and divide decimals

By the end of this section you will know how to:

* Multiply decimals by a 2-digit number without a calculator
* Multiply decimals with up to two decimal places
* Divide decimals by a single-digit number without a calculator

> **Hint**
> The first digit to the right of the decimal point tells you the number of tenths. The second digit tells you the number of hundredths.

### Key points

* When multiplying a decimal by a number, the total number of decimal places in the answer is the same as the total number of decimal places in the calculation.

* When dividing a decimal by an integer, line up the decimal point in the answer with the decimal point in the number being divided when doing short or long division.

**Example**

**1** Work out

**a** $28.4 \times 7$

| $\times$ | 7 |
|----------|-----|
| 20 | 140 |
| 8 | ...... |
| 0.4 | 2.8 |

$28.4 \times 7 = 140 + ...... + 2.8$
$= 198.8$

**b** $3.45 \times 27$

**c** $39.6 \times 1.8$

> **Hint**
> When multiplying decimals, do the multiplication ignoring the decimal points then write the decimal point in the answer.

**Practice**

**2** Work out

**a** $52.3 \times 7$

**b** $89.6 \times 6$

**c** $2.97 \times 34$

**d** $3.55 \times 68$

**e** $4.6^2$

> **Hint**
> $5^2$ means $5 \times 5$.

**f** $2.16 \times 5.24$

**Example**

**3** Work out

**a** $22.5 \div 3$

$$3 \overline{\smash{)}2\,2\,.\,{}^15} \quad = 7\,.\,5$$

**b** $4.55 \div 7$

**c** $\dfrac{82.4}{8}$

> **Hint**
> $\dfrac{82.4}{8}$ is the same as $82.4 \div 8$.

**Practice**

**4** Work out

**a** $56.7 \div 9$

**b** $43.2 \div 6$

**c** $8.05 \div 5$

**d** $\dfrac{3.43}{7}$

**e** $60.16 \div 8$

**f** $\sqrt{1.96}$

**Hint**

Use the $\boxed{\sqrt{}}$ button on your calculator.

**Extend**

**5** Find the total cost of 4 boxes of chocolates at £2.35 each.

**Hint**

In money notation the two digits to the right of the decimal point represent the number of pence, e.g. £0.82 is the same as 82p.

£ .............................

**6** Three friends share a taxi fare equally. The fare is £18.60. How much do they each pay?

£ .............................

| Need more practice | ☐ | Almost there | ☐ | Got it! | ☐ |

# Round decimals

**11.2**

By the end of this section you will know how to:

✳ Round a number to one or two decimal places

**Key points**

✳ The same rules of rounding apply to decimals and whole numbers.

✳ To round to a given number of decimal places, count that number of decimal places from the decimal point. If the **next digit** is:

 • 5, 6, 7, 8, or 9 the digit to be rounded is rounded up

 • 0, 1, 2, 3 or 4 leave the digit to be rounded as it is.

**Example**

**1** Write the following numbers correct to two decimal places.

**a** 4.568

   4.568 → 4.57

**b** 21.193

   21.193 → ...............

**c** 5.065

   5.065 → ...............

**2** Write the following numbers correct to one decimal place.

**a** 45.326

   45.326 → 45.3

**b** 5.17

   5.17 → ...............

**c** 7.446

   7.446 → ...............

**Practice**

**3** Write these numbers correct to two decimal places.

**a** 13.536

**b** 24.342

**c** 29.845

.............................          .............................          .............................

4 Write these numbers correct to one decimal place.

a 11.368 ......................

b 35.754 ......................

c 27.209 ......................

---

Need more practice ☐    Almost there ☐    Got it! ☐

# Add and subtract decimals

**11.3**

By the end of this section you will know how to:

* Add and subtract decimals

## Key points

* When adding and subtracting decimals you need to line up the decimal points so that the place values match.

*Example*

1 Work out

a 32.47 + 5.9

```
    3 2 . 4 7
  +   5 . 9 0
  ........ . 3 7
          |
```

b 271.6 + 12.82

```
    2 7 1 . 6 0
  +   1 2 . 8 2
  ............... . ..... 2
              |
```

c 104.63 + 49.8

```
    1 0 4 . 6 3
  +   4 9 . 8 0
  ............... . ..... 3
```

2 Work out

a 30 − 2.45

```
            |
    3 0 . 0 0
  −   2 . 4 5
  _____ .
```

b 12.72 + 4.6 − 11.96

```
    1 2 . 7 2
  +   4 . 6 0
  _____
```

..........................
```
  − 1 1 . 9 6
  _____
```

**Hint**
In Q2b first do the addition then the subtraction.

c 3.9 − 8.4

```
    8 . 4
  − 3 . 9
  ____ .
```

**Hint**
Q2c will give a negative answer. Do the subtraction the other way round and put a negative sign in front of your answer.

d −15 − −3.2

e −12.4 + −6.3

**Hint**
To subtract a negative you add. To add a negative you subtract.

so answer is ..........................

*Practice*

3 Work out

a 27.8 + 5.93

b 45.8 − 7.63

c 5.61 − 9.3

..................

..................

..................

d 14.8 + 3.54 − 11.96

e 25 + −6.4

f −8.4 + 13.21 − 0.15

..................

..................

..................

**Extend**

4 Paving slabs cost £9.26 each. Work out the total cost of 34 paving slabs.

£ ...........................

## Don't forget!

* How many decimal places will there be in the answer to 28.6 × 3.12? ................

* 53.4 ÷ 6 = ................

* 76.053 rounded to two decimal places is ................ and to one decimal place is ................

* When adding and subtracting decimals you need to line up ...................................

* 3.7 − 9.4 will give a ........................ answer so work out 9.4 − 3.7 and put a ........................ in front of the answer.

## Unit test

1 **a** Work out   12.5 + 6.82 − 11.43          **b** Work out   35.72 + 264 + 3.2 − 97.26

............................              ............................

2 **a** Work out   12.6 × 2.7          **b** Work out   86.1 ÷ 7

............................              ............................

3 **a** Find the value of $5.2^2$          **b** Find the value of $\sqrt{1.44}$

............................              ............................

4 **a** Work out   20 − 4.52          **b** Work out   4.9 − 8.7

............................              ............................

5 **a** Write 2.687 correct to two decimal places.   **b** Write 2.687 correct to one decimal place.

............................              ............................

# Round to one significant figure

## 12.1

By the end of this section you will know how to:

* Round a number to one significant figure

**Key points**

* To round a number to one **significant figure** (s.f.), look at the **second** significant figure:
  * if it is 5, 6, 7, 8, or 9 round the first significant figure up
  * if it is 0, 1, 2, 3 or 4 leave the first significant figure as it is.

* If the first significant figure is in the 10s column you round to the nearest 10, if it is in the 100s column you round to the nearest 100 and so on.

* For a decimal number less than 1 (0. ...) the first significant figure is the first **non-zero** digit to the right of the decimal point.

**Example**

**1** Round the following numbers to one significant figure.

**a** 346

346

answer = 300

**b** 47

47

answer = ...........................

**c** 6.23

6.23

answer = ...........................

**2** Round the following numbers to one significant figure.

**a** 0.3612

0.3612

answer = 0.4

**b** 0.0437

0.0437

answer = ...........................

**c** 0.001 83

0.001 83

answer = ...........................

**Practice**

**3** Round the following numbers to one significant figure.

**a** 4736

...........................

**b** 28.25

...........................

**c** 3.462

...........................

**d** 0.527

...........................

**e** 0.0784

...........................

**f** 0.006 39

...........................

## 12.2

# Estimate answers

By the end of this section you will know how to:

* Estimate answers to calculations by rounding to one significant figure

**Example**

### Key points

* To find estimates for answers to calculations, you can round each number to one significant figure which makes it easier to do the calculation without a calculator.

**1** Work out an estimate for these calculations.

    **a** $28 \times 342$

       $30 \times 300 = \ldots\ldots$

    **b** $609 \times 8.93$

       $600 \times \ldots\ldots = \ldots\ldots$

    **c** $\dfrac{48.8 \times 12.6}{4.5}$

       $\dfrac{\ldots\ldots \times \ldots\ldots}{\ldots\ldots} = \ldots\ldots$

    **d** $49 \times 0.19$

       $\ldots\ldots \times \ldots\ldots = \ldots\ldots$

**Practice**

**2** Work out estimates for these calculations.

    **a** $35 \times 1078$

    **b** $62 \times 4505$

    **c** $382 \times 19.27$

    **d** $\dfrac{8.7 \times 12.06}{11.42}$

    **e** $\dfrac{15.2 \times 0.47}{9.7}$

    **f** $\dfrac{426 + 167.5}{9.7 + 22.1}$

> **Hint**
> First work out the estimated answers for the numerator (top line) and the denominator (bottom line) then divide.

**Extend**

**3** Work out an estimate for the value of $(0.46 \times 0.64)^2$.

**4** Max estimates the value of $\dfrac{249 \times 1.8}{14.7}$ as 60. Lily says it should be 40. Who is correct? You must show your working.

## Don't forget!

* Choose the correct answer from the numbers in the box and complete each statement below.

| 0.03 | 0.3 | 3 | 30 | 40 | 300 | 380 | 400 | 5000 | 5180 | 5200 | 6000 |
|------|-----|---|----|----|-----|-----|-----|------|------|------|------|

- 38 to one significant figure is ..........................

- 376 to one significant figure is ..........................

- 5176 to one significant figure is ..........................

- 0.281 to one significant figure is ..........................

- 0.0326 to one significant figure is ..........................

* For each calculation ring the correct estimation to one significant figure.

**43 × 691**          40 × 700          40 × 690

**376 × 8.19**        400 × 8          400 × 9

$\dfrac{\textbf{59.4} \times \textbf{13.6}}{\textbf{6.8}}$   $\dfrac{60 \times 14}{6}$   $\dfrac{60 \times 20}{7}$   $\dfrac{60 \times 10}{7}$

**0.176 × 0.089**     0.2 × 0.1          0.2 × 0.09

## Unit test

**1** Work out an estimate for $\dfrac{318 \times 42}{5.7}$

..........................

**2** Work out an estimate for $\dfrac{35.2 \times 8.7}{5.8}$

..........................

**3** Work out an estimate for $\dfrac{312 + 456.7}{2.9 + 7.3}$

..........................

**4** Work out an estimate for $\dfrac{0.32 \times 573.8}{11}$

..........................

# 13.1 Use fractions to compare quantities

By the end of this section you will know how to:

✳ Find a fraction of a quantity

✳ Solve fraction problems

## Key points

✳ You can find a fraction of a quantity by using multiplication of fractions.

✳ You can use fractions to solve problems.

> **Hint**
>
> To find a fraction of a quantity, divide by the bottom and multiply by the top.

**Example**

**1** Work out

   **a** $\frac{3}{4}$ of 60

       $60 \div 4 =$ .......

       ....... $\times 3 =$ .......

   **b** $\frac{5}{8}$ of 72

       $72 \div$ ....... $=$ .......

       ....... $\times$ ....... $=$ .......

> **Hint**
>
> To find $\frac{1}{4}$ of something divide by 4.
> To find $\frac{3}{4}$ of something divide by 4 and multiply by 3.

**2** Which is larger, $\frac{2}{3}$ of 45 or $\frac{5}{6}$ of 42? You must show your working.

   $45 \div$ ....... $=$ .......     ....... $\times$ ....... $=$ .......       $42 \div$ ....... $=$ .......    ....... $\times$ ....... $=$ .......

   so ........................................... is larger than ...........................................

**Practice**

**3** Work out $\frac{3}{7}$ of £56.

£ ........................

**4** Work out $\frac{4}{5}$ of £85.

£ ........................

**5** Work out $\frac{7}{12}$ of £144.

£ ........................

**Extend**

**6** A clothes shop gives a student discount of $\frac{1}{8}$ off the price.

A student buys a dress with a price of £128.

How much does she have to pay?

> **Hint**
>
> You need to subtract the discount from the price.

£ ........................

**7** Karl earned £600 last week.

He spent $\frac{1}{3}$ of his wage on some new clothes.

He spent $\frac{1}{4}$ of his wage on entertainment.

What fraction of his wage did he have left.?

**Hint**

Find the total fraction that he has spent then take this away from 1 where $1 = \frac{12}{12}$

Need more practice ☐  Almost there ☐  Got it! ☐

## Express one number as a fraction of another

**13.2**

By the end of this section you will know how to:

✱ Write one amount as a fraction of another amount

**Key points**

✱ For comparisons involving measure make sure the amounts are in the same units.

**Example**

**Practice**

**1** Write 20 as a fraction of 500.

$$\frac{20}{500} = \frac{2}{50} = \frac{1}{\dots}$$

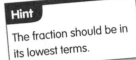

**Hint**

The fraction should be in its lowest terms.

**2** Write 50 cm as a fraction of 3 m.

$3\,m = \dots\dots\dots\, cm$     $\frac{50}{\dots} = \frac{\dots}{\dots}$

**3** Write 10 minutes as a fraction of 3 hours.

**Hint**

You can use the fraction key on your calculator to show a fraction in its simplest form by pressing the ⊟ key.

**4** Write 20 g as a fraction of 1 kg.

**5** In each of the following, write the first quantity as a fraction of the second quantity.

Write your answer in its simplest form.

**a** £2.50,       £10       ........................

**b** 12 ml,       20 ml       ........................

**c** 6 days,      2 weeks      ........................

**d** 45 cm,       1.5 m       ........................

**e** 360 m,       1 km       ........................

**f** 45 minutes,   $2\frac{1}{2}$ hours     ........................

## Unit test

**1  a**  Which is the larger fraction, $\frac{3}{4}$ or $\frac{7}{8}$? Show working to explain your answer.

......................................

**b**  Which is larger, $\frac{4}{5}$ of 60 or $\frac{7}{8}$ of 64? You must show your working.

......................................

**2**  Which is the larger fraction, $\frac{7}{10}$ or $\frac{3}{4}$? You must show your working.

......................................

**3  a**  Write 60 m as a fraction of 3 km. Give your fraction in its simplest form.

......................................

**b**  Write 500 ml as a fraction of 2 litres. Give your fraction in its simplest form.

......................................

**4**  Matthew earns £30 one weekend. He gives £5 to his sister. Express £5 as a fraction of £30. Give your answer in its simplest form.

......................................

**5**  A smartphone normally costs £450. This cost is reduced by $\frac{1}{10}$ in a sale. Find the cost of the smartphone in the sale.

£ ......................................

# 14.1 Find percentages of quantities

By the end of this section you will know how to:

＊ Find a percentage of a quantity

## Key points

＊ There are a number of different ways to work out a percentage of an amount:

- when using a calculator, change the percentage to a fraction or decimal then multiply by the amount
- or, when using a calculator, you can multiply the amount by the percentage then press the percentage key on your calculator
- when not using a calculator, first work out 10% and build up the percentage.

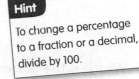

**Hint**
To change a percentage to a fraction or a decimal, divide by 100.

**Hint**
$10\% = \frac{1}{10}$ so to find 10% of an amount, divide by 10.

**Hint**
Instead of $\frac{70}{100}$ you could use $\frac{7}{10}$ or 0.7.

**Example**

**1** Find 70% of 120.

   **a** using a calculator     $\frac{70}{100}$ ☒ 120 = .........

   **b** using the ☒% key     120 ☒ 70 ☒%     answer = .........

   **c** without a calculator     10% of 120 = .........     so 70% = 7 × ......... = .........

**Practice**

**2** Work out

   **a** 45% of 400             **b** 55% of 60

.....................................               .....................................

**3** Work out

   **a** 15% of £80             **b** 35% of £120

£ .....................................        £ .....................................

**4** Which is larger

   **a** $\frac{2}{3}$ of 60 or 70% of 55

.....................................

   **b** $\frac{2}{5}$ of 50 or 45% of 60?

.....................................

# 14.2 Write one number as a percentage of another

By the end of this section you will know how to:

* Write one quantity as a percentage of another

## Key points

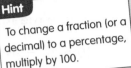

**Hint**
To change a fraction (or a decimal) to a percentage, multiply by 100.

* To write one quantity as a percentage of another quantity:
  * write down the first quantity as a fraction of the second quantity
  * convert the fraction to a percentage.
* For comparisons involving measure make sure the amounts are in the same units.

**Example**

**1** Write

**Hint**
When working without a calculator try writing the fraction as an equivalent fraction with a denominator of 100, then the answer is the numerator.

a  32 as a percentage of 50     $\dfrac{32}{50} = \dfrac{........}{100}$     answer = ............ %

b  11 as a percentage of 20     $\dfrac{11}{20} = \dfrac{........}{100}$     answer = ............ %

**2** Work out

a  20 centimetres as a percentage of 4 metres

4 m = .......... cm     $\dfrac{20}{........} \times 100 = ........$ %

b  15 minutes as a percentage of 2 hours

2 hours = .......... min     $\dfrac{15}{........} \times 100 = ........$ %

**Practice**

**3** Write

a  18 as a percentage of 300

b  4 as a percentage of 25

........................% 

........................%

**4** Work out

a  80 grams as a percentage of 2 kilograms

b  400 metres as a percentage of 5 kilometres

........................% 

........................%

**Extend**

**5** 180 of the 600 people in a cinema are children. Work out 180 as a percentage of 600.

........................%

## Don't forget!

✳ Complete the statements below using the words and numbers in the box.

| 2 | 2 | 10 | 10 | divide | multiply |
|---|---|----|----|--------|----------|

- To find 20% of a quantity find 10% by dividing by .......... then ........................ by ..........
- To find 5% of a quantity find 10% by dividing by .......... then ........................ by ..........

✳ Complete the following:

40% = ⎯⎯ as a fraction = ........................ as a decimal.

✳ Which is the correct calculation to work out 65% of £90?

$\frac{90}{65} \times 100$        $\frac{65}{100} \times 90$        $\frac{65}{90} \times 100$

✳ Which is the correct way to calculate 600 millilitres as a percentage of 4 litres?

$\frac{600}{4} \times 100$        $\frac{4}{600} \times 100$        $\frac{600}{400} \times 100$        $\frac{600}{4000} \times 100$

## Unit test

1 Work out 60% of £120.

£ ........................

2 Work out 5% of £30.

% ........................

3 Work out 40% of £120.

£ ........................

4 Write £15 as a percentage of £60.

........................ %

5 Which is larger

$\frac{3}{5}$ of £80 or 70% of £75? You must show your working.

........................

6 Work out 60 centimetres as a percentage of 5 metres.

........................ %

7 Work out 20% of £350.

£ ........................

8 Work out 15% of £560.

£ ........................

Need more practice ☐    Almost there ☐    Got it! ☐

## Use direct proportion

**15.1**

By the end of this section you will know how to:

✷ Use the unitary method to solve direct proportion problems

**Example**

### Key points

✷ Use the **unitary** method, which means finding the cost of one item

> **Hint**
> Q1 is an example of the **unitary** method.

**1** Five pens cost 65p. Work out the cost of seven of these pens.

5 pens cost 65p          1 pen costs $\frac{65}{......}$ = ......          7 pens cost ...... × 7 = ...... p

**2** Three sandwiches cost £3.60. How much do five sandwiches cost?

3 sandwiches cost £3.60     1 sandwich costs ..................     5 sandwiches cost £ ................

**3** A recipe for 12 cupcakes uses 100 grams of flour.
How much flour is needed for 24 cupcakes?

> **Hint**
> Q3 is an example of the **ratio** method.

24 ÷ 12 = ........          so amount of flour needed = 100 × ........ = .......... g

**4** A recipe for beef stew for 6 people uses 800 g of beef.
How much beef is needed for 9 people?

> **Hint**
> 9 = 6 + 3 so instead you could add half the amount of beef again to 800 g, i.e. 800 + 400 = 1200 g.

9 ÷ 6 = ........          so amount of beef needed = ........ × ........ = .............. g

**Practice**

**5** Four tins of paint cost £12.80. How much do 9 tins of paint cost?

£ ...........................

**6** Three metres of curtain material costs £14.40.
How much do 10 metres of curtain material cost?

£ ...........................

**7** Twelve cream cakes cost £14.40. How much do 8 cream cakes cost?

£ ...........................

**8** Jon is paid £56 for 8 hours' work. How much is he paid for 5 hours' work?

£ ...........................

9  A recipe for 20 shortbread biscuits needs 125 g of butter.
   Kerry uses 250 g of butter. How many shortbread biscuits does she make?

   ..............................

10  Michelle buys 3 identical folders. The total cost of these 3 folders is £5.25.
    Work out the cost of 7 of these folders.

    £..............................

11  A recipe for 10 flapjacks uses 80 g of rolled oats. What weight of rolled oats is needed to make
    15 flapjacks?

    ..............................g

## Simplifying algebraic expressions

**16.1**

By the end of this section you will know how to:
* ∗ Simplify algebraic expressions with only one letter
* ∗ Simplify expressions involving two letters by collecting like terms

**Key point**

* ∗ If you are asked to 'simplify' it means you have to write it in a shorter form.

**Example**

**1** Simplify.

**a** $h + h + h + h$
$h + h + h + h = 4h$

**b** $y + 2y + 5y$
$y + 2y + 5y = $ .......... $y$

> **Hint**
> $1 + 2 + 5 = $ ......

**c** $10w + 3w - 7w$
$10w + 3w - 7w$
$= 13w - 7w$
$= 6w$

**d** $9m - 3m + 7m - 8m$
$9m - 3m + 7m - 8m$
$= 9m + 7m - 3m - 8m$
$= 16m - 11m$
$= 5m$

> **Hint**
> You can add and subtract the terms in any order as long as each term keeps its own sign.

**Practice**

**2** Simplify.

**a** $y + y + y + y + y = $ ...............................

**b** $t + t + t = $ .................

**c** $6c + c = $ .................

**d** $4r + 3r + 2r = $ .......................

**e** $x + 7x + 4x = $ ....................

**f** $15m - m - 4m - 2m = $ .............................

**3 a** $10b - 6b = $ .......................

**b** $17h - 2h - 6h = $ ....................

**c** $7n + 4n - 5n = $ .......................

**d** $8k - 3k + 6k = $ .......................

**e** $14y - 3y + 5y - 8y = $ .......................

**f** $10w - 2w - 6w + 3w = $ .......................

## Using a formula given in words

**16.2**

By the end of this section you will know how to:
* ∗ Substitute numbers into a word formula

**Key points**

* ∗ A formula is a mathematical relationship expressed in words or symbols.
* ∗ A word formula uses words to show the relationship
  e.g. Area of a rectangle = length × width

**1** Work out the perimeter of a square using the formula:
Perimeter = 4 × length of one side
**a** when the square has a side of 3 cm

Perimeter = 4 × 3 = ......... cm

**b** when the square has a side of 4.5 cm

Perimeter = 4 × 4.5 = .......... cm

**2** Lucy works out her pay using this formula:
Pay = Number of hours worked × Rate of pay per hour + Bonus

Work out her pay when she works for 8 hours at a rate of £7 per hour and she gets a bonus of £5.
Pay = Number of hours worked × Rate of pay per hour + Bonus
　　= 8 × £7 + £5

　　= £ ............... + £5

　　= £ ...............

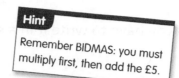

> **Hint**
>
> Remember BIDMAS: you must multiply first, then add the £5.

**3** The total cost of hiring a car can be worked out using this formula:
Total cost = Number of days × Cost per day

**a** Work out the total cost of hiring a car for 8 days at £12 per day.
Total cost = Number of days × Cost per day
Total cost = 8 × 12

　　　　= £ ...............

**b** The total cost was £117 and the cost per day was £9.
For how many days was the car hired?

Total cost = Number of days × cost per day
　　　117 = Number of days × 9

Number of days = ...............

　　　　　= ...............

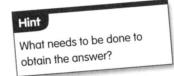

> **Hint**
>
> What needs to be done to obtain the answer?

**4** The total cost of a monthly phone bill is worked out using this formula:
Total bill = Number of minutes × Cost per minute + Monthly charge

Work out the total cost for this phone plan.
The monthly charge is £15.
The number of minutes used is 400.
The cost per minute is 6p.

Total bill = Number of minutes × Cost per minute + Monthly charge

　　= ...............................................................................................

　　= ...............................................................................................

　　= ...............................................................................................

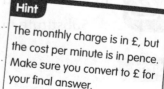

> **Hint**
>
> The monthly charge is in £, but the cost per minute is in pence. Make sure you convert to £ for your final answer.

**5** Lily uses this formula to work out the time taken to cook roast beef:
Time in minutes = 14 minutes per pound + 25 minutes

Work out the cooking time for a joint of beef that weighs 4 pounds.
Time in minutes = 14 minutes per pound + 25 minutes

　　= ...............................................................................

　　= ...............................................................................

**6** Use this formula to work out the average speed of these journeys.

$$\text{Average speed} = \frac{\text{Total distance travelled}}{\text{Total time taken}}$$

**a** 180 miles from Bath to Manchester in 3 hours.

$$\text{Average speed} = \frac{\text{Total distance travelled}}{\text{Total time taken}}$$

$$= \text{.............................}$$

$$= \text{.............................}$$

**b** A sponsored walk of 14 miles that takes 4 hours.

$$\text{Average speed} = \frac{\text{Total distance travelled}}{\text{Total time taken}}$$

$$= \text{.............................}$$

$$= \text{.............................}$$

**c** London to Paris by rail, 300 miles in $2\frac{1}{2}$ hours.

$$\text{Average speed} = \frac{\text{Total distance travelled}}{\text{Total time taken}}$$

$$= \text{.............................}$$

$$= \text{.............................}$$

Need more practice ☐   Almost there ☐   Got it! ☐

# 16.3 Using an algebraic formula

By the end of this section you will know how to:

✶ Substitute numbers into an algebraic formula

**Key points**

✶ An algebraic formula is a mathematical relationship expressed in symbols (letters).

✶ Replace the letters by the numbers given and use BIDMAS to work out the answer.

**Example**

**1** Use the formula $d = 5t$

**a** to work out $d$ when $t = 3$
$d = 5t$
$d = 5 \times 3$

$d = \text{..........}$

**b** to work out $d$ when $t = -6$
$d = 5t$
$d = 5 \times -6$

$d = \text{..........}$

**2** In this question $p = 3$ and $w = 5$.
Work out

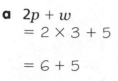

**a** $2p + w$
= $2 \times 3 + 5$

= $6 + 5$

= ....................

**b** $4p + 7w$
= $4 \times 3 + 7 \times 5$

= $12 +$ .........

= ....................

**c** $9p - 2w$
= $9 \times 3 - 2 \times 5$

= ......... $-$ .........

= ....................

**3** In this question $m = 4$, $h = 2$ and $y = 3$.
Work out

**a** $4m$
= ....................

**b** $2m + h$
= ....................

= ....................

**c** $5h + y$
= ....................

= ....................

**d** $4y - 2m$
= ....................

= ....................

**e** $6h + 2y$
= ....................

= ....................

**f** $5m - 3y$
= ....................

= ....................

**4** Use the formula $T = 2k + 3g$ to work out $T$ when:

**a** $k = 5$ and $g = 2$
$T = 2k + 3g$

$T =$ ....................

$T =$ ....................

$T =$ ....................

**b** $k = 6$ and $g = 5$
$T = 2k + 3g$

$T =$ ....................

$T =$ ....................

$T =$ ....................

**c** $k = 4$ and $g = -3$
$T = 2k + 3g$

$T =$ ....................

$T =$ ....................

$T =$ ....................

**5** Use the formula $V = 5w - 2h$ to work out $V$ when:

**a** $w = 4$ and $h = 6$
$V = 5w - 2h$

$V =$ ....................

$V =$ ....................

$V =$ ....................

**b** $w = 7$ and $h = 12$
$V = 5w - 2h$

$V =$ ....................

$V =$ ....................

$V =$ ....................

**c** $w = 2$ and $h = 5$
$V = 5w - 2h$

$V =$ ....................

$V =$ ....................

$V =$ ....................

**6** Use the formula $y = 3x + 8$ to work out $y$ when:

**a** $x = 4$
$y = 3x + 8$

$y =$ ....................

$y =$ ....................

$y =$ ....................

**b** $x = 11$
$y = 3x + 8$

$y =$ ....................

$y =$ ....................

$y =$ ....................

**c** $x = -2$
$y = 3x + 8$

$y =$ ....................

$y =$ ....................

$y =$ ....................

Practice

Use the formula $v^2 = u^2 + 2as$ to find $v$ when $u = 2$, $a = 2$ and $s = 3$.

$v^2 =$ ................

$v^2 =$ ................

$v =$ ................

## Don't forget!

* Simplify:

  $4x + 5x - 6x =$ ............................    $3x - x + 7y =$ ............................

* Work out the perimeter of an equilateral triangle using the formula

  Perimeter $= 3 \times$ length of one side

  when the length of the side is 5 cm.

* Use the formula $P = 2a + b$ to work out $P$ when $a = 3$ and $b = 4$.

## Unit test

**1** Simplify.

  **a** $x + x + x - x$                    **b** $3r + 2r + r$

  = ................                        = ................

  **c** $5m - 2m + 6m$                     **d** $5g + 3g - 4g$

  = ................                        = ................

**2** The total cost of staying in a hotel can be worked out using this formula:

  Total cost = Number of nights $\times$ Cost per night

  **a** Work out the total cost of a 4 night stay in a hotel that costs £52 per night.

    Total cost = ................

  **b** The total cost of a 6 night stay is £366.
     How much does the hotel cost per night?

    Cost per night = ................

**3** In this question $x = 2$, $y = 5$ and $z = 1$.
   Work out

  **a** $5y - z$              **b** $3x + z + y$              **c** $3x - 8z$

    = ................          = ................              = ................

**4** Use the formula $S = 7u + 3v$ to work out $S$ when:

  **a** $u = 2$ and $v = 5$        **b** $u = 6$ and $v = 3$        **c** $u = 4$ and $v = 9$
      $S = 7u + 3v$                   $S = 7u + 3v$                   $S = 7u + 3v$

    $S =$ ................          $S =$ ................          $S =$ ................

# Number Test
## Section A (Non-Calculator)

Time: 1 hour

**1 a** Work out   24.5 + 12.7

.................................................
(1)

**b** Work out   732 − 89

.................................................
(1)

**c** Work out   73 × 100

.................................................
(1)

**d** Work out   72 ÷ 10

.................................................
(1)

**(Total for Question 1 is 4 marks)**

**2 a** Write 836 in words.

.................................................
(1)

**b** Write 836 to the nearest hundred.

.................................................
(1)

**(Total for Question 2 is 2 marks)**

**3 a** Work out   136 × 4

.................................................
(1)

**b** Work out   702 ÷ 6

.................................................
(1)

**(Total for Question 3 is 2 marks)**

**4 a** Here is a clock face.

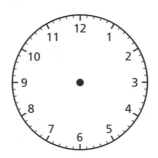

Draw the hands on the clock face to show a time of **twenty-five past nine**.

(1)

**b** Here is a digital clock face.

Write the numbers on the face to show **ten to eight in the evening**.

(1)

**(Total for Question 4 is 2 marks)**

**5** Alex bought 3 pizzas for £2.50 each. He paid with a £10 note.
Work out how much change he should get.

£ ...............................................

**(Total for Question 5 is 2 marks)**

**6 a** Work out $\frac{4}{11} + \frac{3}{11}$

...............................................

(1)

**b** Work out $\frac{7}{8} - \frac{3}{8}$

...............................................

(1)

**(Total for Question 6 is 2 marks)**

**7 a** Write $\frac{1}{10}$ as a decimal.

...............................................

(1)

**b** Write 0.7 as a percentage.

............................................... %

(1)

**c** Write 60% as a fraction.
Write your answer in its simplest form.

...............................................

(2)

**(Total for Question 7 is 4 marks)**

**8 a** Work out   5% of £60

£ ........................................................

(1)

**b** Work out   $\frac{1}{3}$ of 30

........................................................

(1)

**(Total for Question 8 is 2 marks)**

---

**9 a** Write these numbers in order of size. Start with the smallest number.

54     39     8     122     40     109

........................................................

(1)

**b** Write these numbers in order of size. Start with the smallest number.

8.9     0.79     9.8     0.09     7.07     7.2

........................................................

(1)

**c** Write these numbers in order of size. Start with the smallest number.

−3     7     0     −10     4     −1

........................................................

(1)

**(Total for Question 9 is 3 marks)**

---

**10 a** Use rounding to the nearest 10 to find an approximate answer to this question.

49 × 21 = approximately ................... × ................... = ........................................................

(1)

**b** Write a subtraction calculation you could use to check this addition.

24.56 + 18.05 = 42.61

........................................................

(1)

**(Total for Question 10 is 2 marks)**

---

**11 a** Work out   378.6 + 27.35 + 8.42 − 45.68

........................................................

(2)

**b** Work out $35.92 \times 8$

.....................................................................

(2)

**(Total for Question 11 is 4 marks)**

**12 a** Work out $4.8 - 6.3$

.....................................................................

(1)

**b** Work out $-7 - -5$

.....................................................................

(1)

**c** Work out $-8 \times 4$

.....................................................................

(1)

**d** Work out $28 - -7$

.....................................................................

(1)

**(Total for Question 12 is 4 marks)**

**13** Three potted plants cost £4.20
How much would eight potted plants cost?

£.....................................................................

**(Total for Question 13 is 3 marks)**

**14** Work out an estimate for $\dfrac{3.8 \times 44.6}{11.8}$

.....................................................................

**(Total for Question 14 is 3 marks)**

**15** Work out   $378 \times 45$

**16** Here is part of a train timetable from Leeds to Newcastle.

| Leeds | 0922 | 1022 | 1122 | 1222 | 1322 |
|---|---|---|---|---|---|
| York | 0952 | 1052 | 1152 | 1252 | 1352 |
| Northallerton | 1019 | 1119 | 1219 | 1319 | 1419 |
| Darlington | 1031 | 1131 | 1231 | 1331 | 1431 |
| Durham | 1047 | 1147 | 1247 | 1347 | 1447 |
| Chester-le-Street | – | 1153 | – | 1353 | – |
| Newcastle | 1105 | 1206 | 1303 | 1406 | 1505 |

Gemma catches the 1022 train from Leeds to Newcastle.

How long should the train journey take?

(Total for Question 16 is 3 marks)

**17** Simplify $12y - 3y + 5y - 4y$

(Total for Question 17 is 2 marks)

**18** $m = 8$ and $k = 3$
Work out

**a** $7k$

(1)

**b** $5m - 4k$

(2)

(Total for Question 18 is 3 marks)

**TOTAL FOR SECTION A IS 50 MARKS**

# Number Test
## Section B (Calculator)

**Time: 1 hour**

**1** Here is a number line.

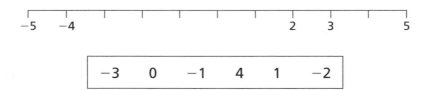

| −3 | 0 | −1 | 4 | 1 | −2 |
|---|---|---|---|---|---|

**a** Write the numbers from the box in the correct places on the number line. Some have been done for you.

(1)

Use your number line to work out

**b** −4 + 6 =

.............................................

(1)

**c** 2 − 5 =

.............................................

(1)

**(Total for Question 1 is 3 marks)**

**2** Colin bought some items at the garden centre.

He bought    3 seed trays at                £2.49 each

4 shrubs at                    £6.75 each

1 bag of potting compost at   £4.95 each

**a** How much did Colin spend?

£ ....................................

(3)

**b** How much change should Colin get from £50?

£ ....................................

(1)

**(Total for Question 2 is 4 marks)**

**3** Here is a list of numbers.

6    11    15    27    30

From the list of numbers

**a** write down a multiple of 9

.................................................

(1)

**b** write down a factor of 24

.................................................

(1)

**c** write down a prime number

.................................................

(1)

**(Total for Question 3 is 3 marks)**

**4** Here is part of a calendar for April 2013.

| April 2013 | | | | | | |
|---|---|---|---|---|---|---|
| **Sun** | **Mon** | **Tues** | **Wed** | **Thurs** | **Fri** | **Sat** |
| | 1 | 2 | 3 | 4 | 5 | 6 |
| 7 | 8 | 9 | 10 | 11 | 12 | 13 |
| 14 | 15 | 16 | 17 | 18 | 19 | 20 |
| | | | | | | |
| | | | | | | |

**a** What day of the week is the 24th April?

.................................................

(1)

**b** What is the date four weeks after the 5th April?

.................................................

(2)

**(Total for Question 4 is 3 marks)**

**5** A jacket costs £90 plus VAT at 20%.

Find 20% of £90

£ .................................................

**(Total for Question 5 is 2 marks)**

**6 a** Use your calculator to work out   112.95 ÷ 15.06

.................................................

(1)

**b** Write 7.829 correct to one decimal place.

.................................................

(1)

**(Total for Question 6 is 2 marks)**

**7** Here is part of the bus timetable from Southampton to Winchester.

| Southampton to Winchester | | | | | | |
|---|---|---|---|---|---|---|
| Southampton | 07:15 | 08:05 | 08:45 | 09:10 | 09:30 | 09:50 |
| Chandler's Ford | 07:47 | 08:38 | 09:18 | 09:38 | 09:58 | 10:18 |
| Otterbourne | 07:57 | 08:47 | 09:27 | 09:47 | 10:07 | 10:27 |
| Winchester | 08:30 | 09:15 | 09:50 | 10:10 | 10:30 | 10:50 |

**a** Which bus should you catch from Southampton to arrive in Winchester for 10 am?

.............................................................

(1)

**b** How long does the 08:05 bus take to get from Chandler's Ford to Otterbourne?

.............................................................

(1)

**c** How long does the 09:50 bus take to get from Chandler's Ford to Winchester?

.............................................................

(1)

**(Total for Question 7 is 3 marks)**

**8** Here is part of Jack's water bill.

```
Water Bill                              September 2012

J. Ashcroft
Greenfield Farm
Billinge

Reading 1st May            1234 units
Reading 1st August         2016 units

Number of units used       _____ units

Cost: £0.05 per unit
```

Work out the total cost of the units used. £ .............................................

**(Total for Question 8 is 4 marks)**

**9** Work out 15% of £40

.............................................

**(Total for Question 9 is 2 marks)**

**10** Work out $\frac{5}{6}$ of £72

.............................................

**(Total for Question 10 is 2 marks)**

11  Which is bigger

$\frac{2}{3}$ of 45   or   70% of 40?

You must show your working.

...........................................................................................

**(Total for Question 11 is 3 marks)**

12  Work out
    a  $7^3$

...........................................................................................

(1)

    b  $\sqrt{196}$

...........................................................................................

(1)

**(Total for Question 12 is 2 marks)**

13  a  Find the value of   $3^2 \times 4^3$

...........................................................................................

(2)

    b  Work out   $\sqrt{5^2 + 12^2}$

...........................................................................................

(2)

**(Total for Question 13 is 4 marks)**

14  a  Write 25 minutes as a fraction of 5 hours.
       Give your answer in its simplest form.

...........................................................................................

(2)

    b  Write 35 cm as a percentage of 7 m.

........................................................................ %

(2)

**(Total for Question 14 is 4 marks)**

**15** Work out $\dfrac{4.8 + 10.4}{2.7}$

   **a** Write down the full calculator display.

.............................................................

(1)

   **b** Give your answer correct to 2 decimal places.

.............................................................

(1)

**(Total for Question 15 is 2 marks)**

---

**16** Harry works out his pay for the week using this formula,

    Pay = Number of hours worked × Rate of pay per hour + Bonus

Harry's rate of pay is £9.30 per hour.
Work out Harry's pay in a week where he works 35 hours and gets a bonus of £15.

.............................................................

**(Total for Question 16 is 3 marks)**

---

**17** Amy got £80 for her birthday.

She spent $\dfrac{1}{4}$ of the money on clothes.

She spent $\dfrac{1}{5}$ of the money on CD's.

What fraction of the money did she have left?
Give your answer as a fraction in its simplest form.

.............................................................

**(Total for Question 17 is 4 marks)**